If You Can't Measure It... Maybe You Shouldn't

Reflections on Measuring Safety, Indicators, and Goals

© 2019 Mind The Risk

First edition

www.mindtherisk.com

info@mindtherisk.com

ISBN 978-82-690377-2-2

Beginners do it qualitative, pros cheat with numbers.

Foreword(s)

You drive to your job on a beautiful Monday morning. The speedometer shows a steady just-below-50 km/h. On the radio, the newsreader tells you about the unemployment figures, the number of casualties of an earthquake in South-East Asia, and that the Dow Jones has fallen some points. Upon entering the gate of your company, you pass a sign that proudly announces that today is the 314th day since the last Lost Time Injury. In the hallway, you see the LEAN Kanban board that shows, among other things, production figures and sick leave statistics. At 8:30, you are all expected to gather around the board and discuss what is presented there. In the elevator to your floor, you quickly check what has happened on Linkedin. You are pleased to see the number of 'likes' that your latest post has drawn. You walk on to your desk where you see a pile of papers. On the top is a copy of the newest balanced scorecard that your boss's secretary must have dropped there, Friday afternoon. While sipping your first coffee of the day, you check your calendar and are reminded of the annual performance review at 10 O'clock.

So far, you have not done one tiny piece of actual work, but you have been confronted with a mass of figures, measurement and metrics already. They are around us, all the time. But why? Do they help? How to deal with them? This little book intends to help you think about them in different, maybe better, ways and handle them better.

By no means is this book intended as a complete treatise on measuring, indicators, goals, metrics, and statistics and so on. These subjects are far too vast for that in one-hundred-something pages. But it will probably address all the main areas and give you some suggestions and tools to think critically about what you come across in your everyday work (or just everyday life), and from there try to find better, more useful ways.

The structure of this book is that of a toilet book, a term that I came across when reading Ben Goldacre's *I Think You'll Find It's A Bit More Complicated Than That* which he calls his "statistics toilet book". Because of this structure, this is one of those books that you do not need to read from start to end, instead you can pick single chapters and read them as they are. You can hop. You can browse. However, to accommodate those who want to read this book the traditional way, I have some more introductory chapters at the start, and some recommendations at the end. In-between however, it is free flow and frequent change.

For those who think that reading on the toilet is disgusting, and since I'm afraid that in the end some of the stories in this book became too long, we can also regard it as a bedtime story safety book. Or as a book to read on your commute by train or tram. On your next trip by plane, or to kill the boring hour(s) on the airport before that flight.

Any which way: another point of the book is that learning about safety can be entertaining. We learn not only from theory. We often learn even more from stories, so I try to weave some learning points (and theory) into stories. If you are looking for the meatier stuff underneath, follow the endnotes for each chapter ('story') where you can find references and additional reflections, in-depth comments and discussions.

In case some parts may appear familiar, the book is partly based on the *Indicators and Measurement* chapter from *Safety Myth 101*, combined with various later writings and ideas around the same subject. So for those who are not interested in a wide spectrum of myths, but rather want something more focused on one subject (which is broad enough as it is, of course), here is a more cost-effective alternative!

There may be a certain repetition of subjects between the 30 (ish) short chapters in this book. This is done intentionally because you should be able to read the chapters separately. However, there will also be some references from one chapter to the other, although I have tried to keep this to a minimum.

Much of what follows may sound a tad negative or critical, I am sorry about that. The aim is to offer a critical view of the subjects discussed and nudge the reader to reflect about measurements, numbers, metrics and indicators. This leads us to discussions of upsides, downsides and some pitfalls. Eventually it may also lead us to thinking about different ways. The aim of the book is not necessarily to provide answers. In the first place I hope it suggests better, or at least different, questions and better/other ways to think about measurements and related topics, as well as giving us a greater sense of humility when applying our tools. And, as mentioned before, at the end of the book (and sprinkled in-between) I will actually offer some suggestions for doing things differently, which may or may not be better. I challenge you to find out.

###

Measuring, why and how

-Measurement- -Control- -Benchmark-

Measuring safety is a source for many misunderstandings. In this book, we will discuss measuring in general, and ask questions like how we should measure. Do we need numbers[1], and are there alternatives? We will look into (safety) goals and incentive schemes that are used to facilitate reaching our goals. We will look at how things are presented, and what they may mean. And of course we will discuss various options with regard to how safety should or could be measured (including the classic subject of measuring unsafety instead of safety), what indicators to use and how useful it is to compare ourselves to others.

First a few starting comments.

Why do we measure at all?

Often a good start to think critically about things is asking 'why'. Why are we so obsessed with measurements and numbers? Why do we spend so much time on these activities?

Below you will find *The Six Key Reasons for Measurement*:

- To monitor
- To comply
- To compare
- To determine direction
- To predict
- To control
- To empower

Hah, fooled you! Of course there is no such thing as *The Six Key Reasons for Measurement*. I just made them up. Also, if you check the list you may notice that there are actually *seven* bullet points. But it worked, did it not? You gave it some extra attention, and the number added some additional weight. We are just in love with numbered lists, telling us about *The X things of Y*. The number adds some science-y sauce and the entire thing looks mightily insightful.

Well, even though there are no *Six Key Reasons for Measurement*, I think the above are good suggestions to think about reasons for measuring. Not necessarily in a particular order and most definitely not assuming completeness. Let us look at them in some more detail.

Monitoring

We measure to determine position, to assess where we are or how things are progressing. Just think of driving your car from A to B, like when you are going on vacation. You watch the signs beside the road to determine how far you have come and how many more kilometres you have to drive. You keep an eye on the fuel indicator on the dashboard to see when you need to fill up gas. You also observe the speedometer in order to keep the speed limit. We try to do much of the same with safety monitoring: whether we are within limits of operation, how we are progressing on action plans, and so on.

Compliance

There are two sides of compliance we can highlight here. Firstly, we have the straightforward meaning. We measure because internal or external authorities require us to do so. This can be government, regulator, the sector, stakeholders, corporate, or management.

The second, less obvious and explicit side is that measuring has become part of our Western/industrial culture. For a good reason, because measuring practices have contributed to our progress during the past centuries. In our common perception, quantitative metrics look scientific and thereby good and reliable. So in a way, by measuring, we comply with societal and cultural expectations[2]. These even go beyond numbers. Quoting Graeber:

> "...the culture of evaluation is if anything even more pervasive in the hyper-credentialized world of the professional classes, where audit culture reigns, and nothing is real that cannot be quantified, tabulated, or entered into some interface or quarterly report."[3]

Comparison

We use our measurements to compare our results or progress to some standard or goal - which we might regard as part of the monitoring process described above, or steering below (several of these reasons overlap, as you will see). Besides that, humans are socially conscious animals (and many of us are also rather competitive), so we tend to compare ourselves to others and use the result to build (or adjust) our self-image - or possibly to argue for or against certain actions. This second kind of comparison is often labelled benchmarking, and we will say more about this later. Finally, we may compare ourselves to ourselves, to see whether we get better or worse.

Steering

Often we measure to determine where we are. Comparing these measurements to a standard, a goal or our previous performance, we can use the results to determine direction and decide on necessary efforts (or maybe a period of relaxing). It helps to show where focus is needed and directs us where to go next (and we implicitly also learn what *not* to prioritise). One of the main drawbacks of using measurements as a way of steering can be that it may swap over into coercion...

Prediction

We also use measurements because we need to know what is going to happen in the future. To assess where will we end up when we continue the course we are on now. What problems are waiting for us in the time to come? Extrapolating past results might help us to prepare for future problems. Sometimes this works fine, like when you monitor the wear on the tyres of your car, you will be able to change them before they wear too thin. But beware, most organizations use past success as an indication that the system is safe and are unable to see when they drift into unsafe working practices[4]. Often we should be rather humble about the predictive and preventive value of our measurements. Swuste cautions about indicators,

> "The main reason why these concepts of ... and safety indicators either have the status of belief, or at least of scientifically unproven links to safety, is because of their weak or absent connection with accident processes."[5]

Controlling

To know gives a feeling of control, and often knowing indeed enables you to control proactively and reactively. You can, to a certain degree, predict what problems to expect. After all, you know what has happened before and can prepare for similar events. This way, you can plan for actions to contain and control these problems, maybe even preventing that they happen at all. Additionally, you can prepare to control the aftermath which may include damage control and covering your behind.

Empowering

It is said that knowledge is power. Measuring enables us to know (or at least gives a sense of knowing) and generally we regard those with knowledge to have an advantage over those that do not. Which makes sense, because if you know what is happening and where you are heading, you may be in a better position to handle a situation. Otherwise, you are merely fumbling in the dark, so to speak.

An interesting aspect here, however, is to consider who actually is empowered by the measurements we perform. In many cases, the measurements and knowledge do not really benefit those who do the actual work. Often the metrics are mainly fodder for 'staffers', bureaucrats or even consultants. Just think of the last time you filled out some meaningless report that you expected no-one would ever do something useful with. Congratulations! You were most likely right about that one...

How do we measure?

Having thought about reasons why we measure, let us have a quick look at how we can measure. There are many variations here, but a basic approach that applies to many situations contains the following elements. We collect data from:

- Existing registrations of data that are already collected in your organisation. Accident reports, hours worked, sick leave, production figures and so on are part of 'business as usual'.
- Automatic registrations. In our highly digitized and automated world we find more and more of these. As for example a flight data recorder that collects a mass of information automatically.
- Things we are interested in but that are not available to us yet and we need to collect actively. For example, by asking workers through questionnaires, audits, workshops and surveys.

Having collected our 'raw' data[6], we categorise and classify the various items, often by adding certain attributes to them. This helps us to divide a mass of data into useful and digestible chunks. This also enables us to do analyses and assessments. For example: when do things happen, what are the major concerns, are there trends and developments, are things connected to certain organisational units, processes, locations or systems, or how is the situation in comparison to a standard or goal?

This process is very useful, but also hides some of the richness of the original data (which is already a simplified version of the real world, of course) as well as that it almost always introduces some biases into the process[7]. We need this higher abstraction in order to make sense of a huge collection of data, but we need to be clear about the loss in information. Often this loss of richness is furthered when the analysis is transformed into numbers, indices and graphs. Or transformed into matrices, colours, smileys, up/down arrows, and the like. Often these are also merely numbers 'in disguise'.

Before we proceed...

A takeaway from this introductory chapter should be that you realise that why you measure and how you measure *will* affect the results. Therefore: be mindful of these effects and take them into account when planning to measure. The second thing we should keep in mind is that even though we may immediately and automatically think about numbers, measurement is not exclusively about numbers. There are other ways, and we use these qualitative ways of measurement all through the day. The thing is that we do not label these processes always as measurements, but rather call them 'assessment' or something similar.

###

[1] By the way, if you want a source for the Thorsten Langenhan quote opening the book, it is from a Linkedin discussion: https://www.linkedin.com/feed/update/urn:li:article:9030312702833892117?commentUrn=urn%3Ali%3Acomment%3A%28article%3A9030312702833892117%2C6560262742287142912%29

[2] We can attribute this very much to our post-enlightenment thinking with a stress on positivism - a view that only empirical science interpreted through reason and logic, forms the exclusive source of all certain knowledge. In its modern form we may also mention of Frederick Taylor whose legacy of Scientific Management affected most areas of our lives, by making things 'scientific' and measurable as well as summing up complex activities into single metrics (like in Taylor's case efficiency).

[3] Graeber, D. (2015) *The Utopia of Rules. On Technology, Stupidity, and the Secret Joys of Bureaucracy*. Brooklyn/London: Melville House.

The quote is from p.41-42.

[4] Woods, D.D. & Cook, R.I. (2002) Nine Steps to Move Forward from Error. *Journal of Cognition Technology and Work*, 4: 137-144.

[5] Swuste, P.H.J.J. (2016) Is Big Data Risk Assessment a Novelty? *Safety and Reliability*, 36 (3): 134-152. doi: 10.1080/09617353.2016.1252084.

The quote is from p.136.

[6] Regarding so-called 'raw data', I came across a quote that was attributed to British social scientist Gregory Bateson (1904-1980). So far, I have been unable to trace its exact origins, but it is too good to leave it unmentioned:

"No data is truly 'raw', and every record has somehow been subjected to editing and transformation either by man or his instruments."

That should keep us a bit more humble about our data, I would say.

[7] See the Bateson quote above, although it would really need at least a chapter of its own. Let me point you at least to a great recent paper on the subject by a team of Dutch researchers:

Burggraaf, J., Groeneweg, J., Sillem, S. & van Gelder, P. (2019) How Cognitive Biases Influence the Data Verification of Safety Indicators: A Case Study in Rail. *Safety*, 69 (5): 1-22. doi: 10.3390/safety5040069.

They identified five pitfalls:

1. *The 'good form as evidence' error*: if data looks good, it is assumed that the quality is good.

2. *The 'improved-thus-correct' fallacy*: if data is improved it is assumed that data quality is good.

3. *Situation-dependent-identity-oversight*: forgetting that data can be different depending upon the situation (e.g. whom it comes from, or when).

4. *Impact underestimation*: assuming that a small variation in a data source corresponds to a small variation in the outcome.

5. *The beaten track disadvantage*: Difficulties in spotting problems when following the narrative of the item that is to be verified.

Measuring what?

-Measurement- -Indicators- -Safety-

All over the place?

During a master class, I asked the audience what safety was to them, and how their organisation measured safety. The whiteboard was quickly filled with a variety of items:

- number of accidents and near-accidents,
- safety talks and experience interviews,
- frequency and severity rates,
- number of high potential learning events / SIF[1],
- employee satisfaction surveys,
- worker engagement,
- progress on improvement actions,
- findings from audit, inspections, observations, safety walks, etc.,
- events with aggression and violence,
- difference between perception of management and experience of workers.

I do not want to do an in-depth analysis of the above and try to put things in categories, but when we allow a minute of reflection upon them, we can see some interesting things:

- passive metrics, which were taken from registers, and active measurements,
- 'hard' (quantitative) and 'soft' (qualitative) measures,
- things that go wrong and things that go right,
- top-down and bottom-up,
- leading and lagging indicators.

Additionally, one of the participants mentioned how the organisation was trying to switch from measuring 'unsafety' (i.e. accidents and incident) to 'safety'. Besides, some participants mentioned safety for their patients and security in addition to the traditional intuitively understood - but often mixed-up - kinds of safety: occupational and process safety.

What is safety anyway?

Before starting to measure, one needs to know what one is measuring. If we want to assess our progress towards our holiday destination, we need to know how to express this and then how to measure or calculate. Are we talking about estimated time needed until arrival? Or distance travelled so far? Or are we instead focusing on the fun we have and the things we see during our journey?

So, what is safety? There are many different views, and we will not discuss all of them extensively at this point. However, I would like to take just a few examples to illustrate the problem. Many others exist, but a few should suffice to make a point. As you will see, none of them will cover the subject entirely and all have advantages and disadvantages.

For this discussion I propose the following three, quite common views on safety:

- Safety is following (safety) rules.
- Safety is the absence of accidents.
- Safety is taking acceptable risk.

You may be familiar with all three, or some, but let us look at them a bit closer.

Safety as compliance

Let us start with a very basic way of thinking about safety: safety is following the safety rules. Period. Being compliant with these rules is being safe. This correspondents to the almost automatic reaction that many people have after an accident: if only they had followed the rules, this would not have happened. If you had not ignored the red man light[2], you would not have been hit by a car. That kind of thinking. Many investigations therefore focus on breaches of protocol and deviations. And also in 'normal' situations there is a major focus on compliance with safety rules. Wear the mandatory safety gear. Hold the railing. Striving for compliance also appeals to the human tendency towards conformity; to follow the herd. We are social creatures, after all.

Safety rules are important for a number of other reasons. It is for a reason that safety rules are one of the most basic forms of how we are taught safety: "Don't touch the stove, it's hot!" "Watch left, right, left before crossing the street." "Red means stop!" These are the things we teach our kids, our workers, people who want to drive a car, and so on. Children need rules because they do not have the experience yet and cannot assess the risks for themselves. But it just goes on as we grow up. Safety rules are not perfect, however. They can never cover all situations, because we cannot think of every possibility up front. If we could, then the rules were impossible to handle because of their sheer volume. Besides, they do depend on context. In London, Hong Kong or

Tokyo, it is smarter to look *right, left, right* before crossing while this is not the best strategy for Amsterdam, Paris or Rome.

Viewing safety as compliance works reasonably well in rather simple, ordered and predictable systems. After all, in these situations you have a reasonable chance to foresee what can happen and conceive actions to deal with variations. Very much comparable to if_then_else routines written for computers. As long as you are on known territory, you can deal with the things that happen by applying prescribed routines and 'best practices'. Following these routines means acting safely, while acting outside of these scripts is regarded as unsafe.

Following safety rules is certainly important, but it is an incomplete way to deal with safety and no guarantee of being 'safe'. Firstly, we live and work in a world with a lot of variability and we have a limited amount of foresight. This means that we cannot write rules for every eventuality. Besides, even if we did, the rulebook would be so huge that no one bothered to open it, or had a chance to find what they needed.

Secondly, rules are compromises[3] and may sometimes not be sufficient to keep you safe. Even if you follow all the traffic rules, you can have an accident. For example, when others do not follow the rules. Or if something very unexpected happens. A known example of compliance that was insufficient to save lives is the Titanic. This ship was perfectly compliant with regard to the number of life boats[4]. Still, hundreds of people lost their lives because not all of them fitted in the life boats available.

In some situations, following rules is even the *unsafe* option. One (in)famous example is the Piper Alpha disaster where the people that followed the emergency procedures died while the ones who ignored the procedures and just jumped overboard survived.

Safety as an absence of accidents

Go out on the street and ask a hundred randomly chosen people the question "What is safety?" Chances are that a substantial part of these (make that the vast majority) will answer something in the line of "Not having any accidents" or "Freedom of harm".

Thinking this way makes intuitively sense to most people. The simple definition of "Safety is not having accidents" feels right because in our minds safety and accidents are very much linked. When we do not have any accidents, we have been safe. Or have we? Actually, not necessarily... That nothing has happened, that there has not been an accident, does not mean that things are safe. In many cases it only means that nothing has happened *yet*. Although it can very well be that nothing happens ever.

A simple test is to reverse the definition, "Safety is the absence of accidents" and see whether it still works. We then get "The absence of accidents is safety". So say there are actually zero accidents connected to an activity, does this logically mean that this activity was safe? What if I have to fix the light in my office, but I do not have the proper tools at hand? Say I climb on an office chair, use a kitchen knife to unscrew the fitting and then fumble with the wiring. The light starts working again, I get down from the chair and exclaim, "There, I fixed it!" Was that safe? Hardly. But I did not experience an accident in this situation, even though we all feel that I really should have.

"Safety is the absence of accidents" feels right, but it does not make logical sense because absence of accidents can be achieved by other ways. Randomness or luck, like in the scenario above, is an important factor. Your definition of accident is another factor. Whether people choose to report accidents yet another.

This is not to say that accidents do not give an indication about safety, or rather unsafety. An accident can be regarded as a manifestation of unsafety[5], or rather of risk which manifests itself. Which is a good transition to the next view on safety.

Safety as acceptable risk

Whatever you do, there is some level of risk involved. We cannot avoid this, and we even want some risk, but not too much. We need to compromise between various goals (financial, safety, production, quality, etc.), between uncertainty and control. We have only limited resources (money, time, expertise, etc.). This means that we have to make trade-offs and find a balance. Therefore, this is a useful view of safety as it may lead to a search to that acceptable level of risk.

Safety-as-acceptable-risk is a view that appeals to rational creatures. It suggests deliberation and decision based on 'facts'. We realise that we always will face risks. We just have to make sure that the risks are not unacceptably high - or in a more positive view: that they are acceptably low. The question is therefore what level is the right level of risk. We should obviously try to put as much 'distance' as possible between ourselves and the hazard and the possible negative futures the hazard could lead to. But we do not want too much distance either. It has to be practicable and affordable. Besides, some hazards we actually *do* desire. Just think of drinking coffee. We want our coffee hot, but we do not want to burn ourselves. Therefore we tend to sip our coffee carefully at first, or maybe blow a bit on it, instead of gulping it down at once.

The view of safety-as-acceptable-risk has much going for it, but there are also some drawbacks. One of these is its reliance on knowledge[6], another is the way it can lead to numerical approaches to risk that look more objective than they are, that it may lead to a static view of safety, and the problem of how to monitor the risk level. Then there is of course the problem of *who* decides what is 'acceptable' and based on *what*. Who determines what is included in the assessment and what factors weigh in (and how much)? Who is allowed to participate in the process and how can they participate in the process. What language is used during the process and in the communication of the results?

One example of the latter is how consequences are selected and expressed. Certain risk assessments focus on fatalities, but those are often not the only bodily consequences. So what to do with injuries? Should one choose a number of severe injuries that equals a fatality? Or should we, as one often sees, translate fatalities and injuries into monetary units? Is that really a good, and fair measure? Can you put a number on a human life? And if so, what number? Sure, you can estimate one person's economic contribution to society and his/her family, but a person is so much more than his/her economic contribution.

Even in situations where it is relatively easy to calculate, and things are expressed in money, measuring risk and assuming objectivity is problematic. Take gambling. Often the odds are known in rather good detail. The consequences (win or lose an x amount of money) are also clear. In theory, the risk can be perfectly calculated: probability times consequence. One number, same for everyone. However, the risk experience is not the same from one person to the other. Value 'x' is not the same from one person to the next. Sure, you may be dealing with 1.000 Dollars in each case, but for one person 1.000 Dollars may be their monthly wage (or more), while for another it is what he or she spends in a random weekend on shoes.

Challenges

The above views of safety all bring their own ways of measuring safety. Regard safety as compliance and you may be tracking citations from the inspectorate, or observations of unsafe acts (e.g. not wearing protective equipment). If safety is seen as the absence of accidents, you will naturally follow up on accident and injury reports. Those who adopted a risk view of safety may have some kind of a risk register, present the most important risks in a risk matrix or heat map and follow up on actions to control the risks.

How you define safety will influence your choice of things you measure - and vice versa! What you measure may very well become your definition of safety, whether you want this or not. Whether this is a conscious choice or (often, I assume) not. If corporate policy, an ISO standard or the regulator requires you to record accidents and near misses as part of your monitoring safety performance, it will become very natural to talk about these metrics when someone asks about "How are we doing at safety?"

Another challenge is that management reports, dashboards, scorecards, or what we choose to call them, tend to allow only limited space for the presentation of how things are going for safety. After all, managers are busy people and they would very much like to get clear, concise, unambiguous and short answer.

However, as the three different views (and other views are possible) tell us that safety is a complex phenomenon, we need a variety of measures to give a reasonable description. No one view captures all of safety, and every view shows some elements but not the full picture. A good answer thus needs rich information and nuances. Here is a tension between space and attention available and what is needed to give a high quality answer.

Dumbing it down into an easy measure, no matter how intuitive, will not do justice to the subject. So when you express safety as some kind of fatality/injury-based metric, you only capture a tiny part of a very complex phenomenon. It would be like describing a river[7] exclusively by its temperature - which, by the way, rather depends on its surroundings, location and season than on 'itself', just as injury rates may correlate stronger with the context than with safety efforts initiated by the organisation. A trade-off between thoroughness and efficiency is inevitable, and taking care to address this in one's management system is essential.

###

---

1 SIF = serious injury and fatality. Please check the later chapter(s) on the subject.

2 Which is perfectly legal in Norway, where I live. However, you are expected to assess the situation whether this can be done safely.

3 We are not going to spell out this point here, but we need to refer to Myth 43 from *Safety Myth 101*.

4 Actually, they had a greater capacity than regulations required at the time. The Titanic is also a known example of improved safety rules *after* an accident. Afterwards standards for life boat capacity increased significantly.

5 Although I am reluctant to say that an accident is automatically the proof of 'unsafety'. But that requires a philosophical discussion that exceeds the scope and size available for this little book…

6 What we do not know or cannot imagine we cannot include in our risk assessment. And sometimes worse, the assumptions we make may determine the risk to a greater degree than the hazards we think we are dealing with.

7 Thanks to Todd Conklin for the river metaphor to discuss the problems of discussing complex phenomena by limited characteristics. You can find it at page 110 of this fine book:

Conklin, T. (2016) *Pre-Accident Investigations: Better Questions*. Boca Raton: CRC Press.

Safety First?[1]

-Priorities- -Safety- -Goals-

This is probably the best known and most widely spread slogan in safety[2]. Often heard and repeated without thinking it through because we consider it as obviously[3] true since we all want to get home in one piece after a day's work, don't we?

So when we say "Safety First", do we really mean what we are saying?

If we do, we would place safety before *everything* else. How realistic is that? And what would it actually mean if we executed this to the letter? Hardly any company would exist for a long time; they would run into financial ruin because all spending went to their prime priority: safety. Please keep in mind that NO organisation exists with the sole objective of being safe. The prime reason for their existence is to deliver some product or service and to make money to provide for its owners, employees and other stakeholders. Safety is an important condition that has to be fulfilled in order to survive, but it is not the prime objective[4].

A Safety Professional[5] once told me:

> "Safety is like salt. You need just the right amount to make your food taste good, put too much salt in it and it will taste awful".

Besides, say that we put safety first... We still have to ask what safety should come first: occupational, transport, process, societal, customer, product, information, environmental, patient? Or just all of them? And is this possible at all?

When we are talking about occupational risk, by the way, we should rather say *Health First* than *Safety First!* At least when looking at the risk and documented consequences[6]. Even though an immediate safety effect may seem so much scarier, slowly creeping health risks over long time have proven to be much more fatal so far[7].

What a "Safety First" slogan *actually* means to say, but muddles the message through its clumsy absolutism, is that there should be some kind of a minimum level of safety that has to be guaranteed as one of the more important requirements for running a business. Do note that this level is often an invisible line that you do not know about until you cross it.

One final thought: if safety really comes first, what comes second?

[1] Based on Myth 70 from *Safety Myth 101*.

[2] Which is not really surprising since 'Safety First' was the tagline attached to the early safety movement in the USA. Fred Lange's handbook on safety from 1926 tells:

> "In America the first notable effort to prevent accidents was undertaken by the United States Steel Corporation in 1907. At the time of its organisation in 1900 it inherited from the H.C. Frick Coke Company the slogan - 'Safety the First Consideration', which had been an operating rule of the Frick Company for a score of years by order of its president, Thomas Lynch." (p.2)

Lange, F.G. (1926) *Handbook of Safety and Accident Prevention*. New York: The Engineering Magazine Company.

Several other early safety thinkers were critical about the slogan (already in the 1920s!) and argued that safety and production should go together. One source as recommended reading on the early days of safety:

Swuste, P.H.J.J., Gulijk, C. van & Zwaard, W. (2010) Safety Metaphors and Theories, a Review of the Occupational Safety Literature of the US, UK and The Netherlands, till the First Part of the 20th Century. *Safety Science*, 48: 1000-1018. doi:10.1016/j.ssci.2010.01.020.

A freely downloadable version can be found at: https://tudelft.openresearch.net/image/2016/11/24/swuste_vangulijk_zwaard_2010_safety_science_48.pdf

Another great source for early safety history:

Aldrich, M. (1997) *Safety First: Technology, Labor, and Business in the Building of American Work Safety, 1870-1939*. Baltimore: Johns Hopkins University Press.

[3] Little is really ever obvious, by the way. Think about it! So we should obviously do our best to use it as little as possible.

[4] Alan Quilley wrote in a mail to me,

> "Many forget that their actually goal is Safe Production. Not just creating safety - then nobody moves and no one gets hurt approach. Eventually this makes companies go broke. Then someone else buys all the stock and fixes the company!"

[5] Sorry, but I really do not recall who it was. But I think it is a brilliant analogy and truly wise words.

[6] See among others the first chapter of Andrew Townsend's book:

Townsend, A.S. (2014) *Safety Can't Be Measured: An Evidence-based Approach to Improving Risk Reduction*. Farnham: Gower Publishing.

[7] Some may try to argue that this is because we placed have safety first, well, that is rain dancing for you.

Measurement: Beware[1]

-Measurement--Indicators--Goals-

Measuring is an activity that seems to come to us quite naturally, so often we do not think an awful lot about it. However, measurements are not without problems. Let us look at some common problems and pitfalls, which we will discuss in some more detail in this book.

Problems and pitfalls

First, are you measuring constructs or 'real' things? While numbers ooze a sense of objectivity and precision, often things are not quite as objective as we think they are. This means we should probably treat them a bit more careful and keep their limitations in mind. And maybe not use them at all.

Second, are we measuring 'the real thing' or do we need to rely on surrogates and proxies? Many things cannot be measured directly - simply because it is not possible, feasible or because it would be unethical. Then we need some kind of replacement that (in all likelihood) has a connection to what we are actually interested in and allows for conclusions about that subject. However, what is the quality of our surrogate?

Where do you put your focus in your measuring? Are you trying to be proactive with leading indicators? Are you looking backwards at how things have been with lagging indicators? Are you measuring actual output and results or mere 'outcomes'? How useful are these measures? And by the way, is there actually a real difference between leading and lagging indicators?

When considering above mentioned factors like surrogates, leading or lagging indicators and usefulness it is important to consider whether our data actually says something about what we need to know. Is there a causal connection, or are we merely seeing correlation?

Probably even more important, are we actually measuring and monitoring the right thing and directing the focus the right way? To use a known example, it is problematic to focus merely on occupational safety metrics when your major hazards come from process safety issues.

Finally, do we understand the number? What does the number tell us? If it is an average, do we actually understand what it means? Is it appropriate to use it the way it is used? Are we using it in a sensible way?

Indicators

You do not necessarily need to measure things in order to manage them, but sometimes it is extremely practical. And that is when good indicators are essential.

Indicators should help us to manage our businesses by giving an indication if things go the right way (or not) such that we - if necessary - can adjust and steer in the right direction[2]. Indicators may therefore be an important element in your improvement cycle.

It is important to realise that we can differentiate between several kinds of indicators. Many people just throw them together and talk about KPIs like every number is a KPI. Well, they are NOT. As a minimum I would like to differentiate between:

- Indicators - a number that may say something, but it is slightly unclear how the effect and causality are. The indicator may be interesting, but in general it is of little use for actually managing safety. Think for example of fatalities or injuries.
- Performance Indicator - an indicator where it is established that it tells us something about our performance. Not only interesting, but often very useful too.
- Key Performance Indicator (KPI) - basically just a performance indicator, but one that is thought to be so important that it is the most important cue for a certain area of performance. This may be very hard to determine. For example because it may be very hard to capture a complex matter like safety in one or just a few indicators.

Side effects

As any action, measurements come with side effects that are worth to reflect on. How do measurements affect us? And how do we affect measurements? Just some immediate thoughts...

Importantly, there is a positive effect because measurements help us to focus. Measurements are an indication of importance, conscious or not, and so people give more or less automatic priority to the things that get measured. A known management dictum claims "What gets measured gets done", and for a reason. This can be used as a powerful driver of what you want to achieve.

However, in that power lies also one of the main potential pitfalls, because when people focus too much on the metric instead of the underlying objective, the means (the measured results) may quickly become an end in themselves. Then, measurement invites to manipulate the results because there may be easier ways to reach the numerical goal than hard work to achieve the underlying objective. In the case of safety, there are ways to get a lower number of accidents without really improving safety at all. My Belgian friend Bart Vanraes wrote an interesting thesis[3] on the subject and coined the term 'Tippex Ongevallen', meaning accidents that are brushed away and hidden from sight, just as the correction fluid (Tipp-ex) does with typos.

Another issue is that numbers look precise, objective and scientific. Even if these are mere estimates, statistically insignificant or based on counting subjective attributions. Numbers seem to give certainty. Because of this we may give them more weight than they should have. They may over communicate their message, just as 'red' indicators may do.

One reason for this over communication is because numbers and metrics apparently simplify an issue. It directs focus, seems to show you where you should pay attention and what to do. However, this is a very reductionist simplification and if you concentrate on what a metric appears to be telling you, you may seriously be missing a point because measurements, data, and metrics need to be seen within their context. Without context, data has no real meaning.

That context is also essential to understand and interpret your data. As mentioned above, are they telling you about a causal connection or merely about correlation? And are they actually telling you something? Your measurements will contain both signal and noise and you may think that you see patterns and trends that do not really exist. This can lead to interventionism or misplaced actions.

With these thoughts in the back of our minds, let us proceed into the wondrous world of measurements, indicators and metrics. Many of the above mentioned concerns we will meet again and elaborate upon.

---

[1] Originally based on the Introduction to the Measurement/Indicators chapter of *Safety Myth 101* but seriously expanded and supplemented with elements from the 'Meten Is Weten?' session at Nyenrode Business University in May 2019.

[2] More or less like a thermostat does at home. You select a desired temperature. When this is reached you thermostat will switch off the heater until the temperature drops below some lower limit and then the thermostat will switch on the heater again and the cycle starts again. Keep in mind that cause and effect relationships in safety will be much more complicated and invisible than this simple process.

[3] Vanraes, B. (2019) *Tippexongevallen: Struisvogelpolitiek in Veiligheidsland*. Eindwerk Preventieadviseur Niveau 2.

Preventable Accidents...[1]

-Statistics- -Accidents- -Prevention-

Early July 2016 the IOSH[2] raised the alarm. "IOSH Says More Action Needed on Preventable Deaths" said the header, "The emphasis comes after an annual rise in work-related deaths in Britain" the press release[3] continued. Now that sounds serious. It also triggers some questions.

Lies, damn lies and...

First question: what does "an annual rise in work-related deaths in Britain" actually mean? Ah, well, the numbers went from 142 one year to 144 next year. In absolute numbers this is indeed a somewhat higher number. But looking at trends (which we should not do from year to year, of course), this is not a rise. In fact, it is a fairly stable level. The slightly higher number is most likely explainable by random fluctuations. As you can read in another story later in this book[4], Norwegian road traffic fatalities went down and up again by 30, and I suppose that the number of Norwegian road users is smaller than the working population in Britain.

Doing just a superficial check (Google for: fatalities + Britain), the first hit brought me to the most recent statistics on fatalities in the workplace in Great Britain 2016. You can download the report[5], or see them online[6]. What do we see? There has been a steady decline in fatalities from the mid-1990s on (with ups and downs, as expected - pity that the HSE did not provide a rolling average), which has been levelling out the past few years. So: a rise? No. Has something dramatic happened? No.

Of course every fatality is one too many. It is a tragedy for the people involved, especially those left behind. But if you want to convey that message that then you should just say so and not wrap it in some nonsense (non-existent) trend.

Another reason to be cautious about these "Cry wolf" press releases is that they may trigger simplistic interventionism which may work entirely counter-effective.

Nonsensical qualifiers

Second question: What does the adjective 'preventable' add?

It is an expression for hindsight, for sure. As that, it gives me a bad taste. It says that 'they' (employers, employees, others?) should have known better. Some of these deaths could have been prevented, if only... And yes, some, maybe even many of them could have been prevented, but what does this conclusion help us? On the positive side it tells us what we can do better next time. On the other, negative side, it's an expression of blame that gives us an adversarial start. Not a good starting point for improvement I would say.

But that is in retrospect. It is also possible to read the IOSH's press release forward looking: "More Action Needed on Preventable Deaths". That raises however another problem. Because, what is a 'preventable death', or more general, a 'preventable accident'? How on earth would you know in advance?

Some may offer the "All Accidents Are Preventable" slogan as an answer. I am not sure if Shelley Frost[7], executive director of policy at IOSH, meant this when she stated that "All deaths are avoidable", but still, do not both statements make the term 'preventable' entirely redundant?

But are they really? All accidents are only preventable if we have full control, full foresight and unlimited resources. Since we have neither of these (after all, we are living in a messy, uncertain world and have to do with limited knowledge, time and resources) not all accidents are preventable.

That does not mean that we should not try to do our utmost, and so I applaud that IOSH is committed "to supporting professionals in building capability within organisations, enabling them to deliver an effective health and safety agenda for their workforce". Which then (hopefully) will prevent many accidents, and harm. But I still wonder about the clumsy, binary and unrealistic use of language. Proper use of language is extremely important for doing effective health and safety work, after all!

And so...

I understand the sentiment and I appreciate the engagement, because every fatality is a tragedy for those involved. I also understand that organisations like IOSH use each and every opportunity to reach the media in order to raise awareness and get attention for safety. Still... I find it rather unprofessional to seek sensation and beat some drum that is not there. Now, I only get a feeling that the IOSH (an organisation that has to stand for quality in the profession!) apparently cannot tell the signal from the noise.

There are ways to address the issue without spinning the information this way. Why not frame the message in line with the facts. For example:

> "We see no improvement..."

> "There are still high levels..."

> "Every fatality is one too many, and therefore..."

And please drop that 'preventable' nonsense. Talking from hindsight is not a good idea.

---

[1] Based on a blog from July 2016 that resonated with many safety professionals.

[2] Institution of Occupational Safety and Health (https://www.iosh.com/)

[3] https://ohsonline.com/articles/2016/07/12/iosh-says-more-action-is-needed-on-preventable-deaths.aspx (checked 20 July 2019)

[4] Look for 'Surrogates'.

[5] http://www.hse.gov.uk/statistics/pdf/fatalinjuries.pdf (checked 23 July 2019)

[6] http://www.hse.gov.uk/statistics/fatals.htm (checked 23 July 2019)

[7] https://www.iosh.co.uk/News/Help-make-Britains-workplaces-even-safer-says-IOSH.aspx (checked in July 2016 when writing the original blog, apparently this news item has been removed in the meantime)

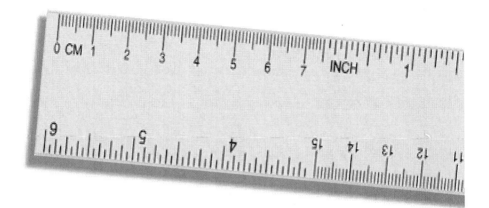

If You Can't Measure It, You Can't Manage It[1]

-Managing- -Measurement- -Monitoring-

Ancient management wisdom says: "If you can't measure it, you can't manage it"[2]. The logical addition then appears to be: "To measure you need numerical goals and indicators". This is a very persistent view propagated through many management courses, MBAs, management-by-objectives guidelines and the New Public Management[3] movement. Quality management guru Deming, however, called this a Myth. In fact, he went as far as calling it a "costly myth"[4]!

I sidle with Deming. The practice of putting measurement on too high a pedestal can be very costly because:

- Collecting and monitoring does not automatically change things for the better - the Hawthorne effect[5] notwithstanding. Hopkins and Maslen[6] say that: "A problem with many numerical performance indicators is that it is not immediately obvious how the activity of a manager may affect it".
- Data does not equal Information and nor do reports imply answers. And it is not even sure that you need answers, often you are better served by questions.
- Companies spend loads of resources collecting data[7], trying to measure something that may or may not be relevant.
- These measures are often no good measures, because one uses some agreed standard measure (e.g. LTIF) or makes use of whatever data is (easily) available - not necessarily data that gives proper information about the subject they are supposed to measure.

- Setting a goal and measure and getting a good score does not automatically improve real performance. Often measures misdirect resources either because they invite to gaming the measure, or because it triggers interventionism[8]. Especially when the measure has become the goal[9]. What you measure is what you get; this is a solution and also a major problem.
- Numbers are not important - the quality of the information[10] is, and what is done with it.
- Another consequence of a focus on measurable items (numbers) is that often, more time is being spent on deciding what should not be part of the statistics, than discussing possible actions for correction or improvement.

Actually, in many instances things seem to be measurable, but it is a mistake to think that measurable equals numbers. There are more creative ways of measuring than counting. Qualitative measurements may seem to be less precise, but are often much more useful[11]. Just think about the 'measurement' you perform before leaving the house in order to decide if you should take an umbrella or not. Besides, qualitative measures have the possibility to give nuance and richness that you just will not be able to find in numbers.

One example is training. This subject has limited opportunities for useful measurement in numerical terms (% of personnel that has received training could be one), but measuring the effect of training in numbers is near impossible (especially when linked to outcome effects - then we have to involve a lot of assumptions and indirect effects). It could, however, be possible to say something in qualitative terms about the effect[12].

Things are nicely summed up by a quote that is often attributed to Albert Einstein[13], "Not everything that can be counted counts and not everything that counts can be counted". And that leads to just another thought, because do our numerical goals really count that much as we think they do? What if all you have is the goal, but are missing a way or strategy to reach that goal?[14]

Mind you, metrics are important, because they help us to make sense of complex matters, they help us to get focus and they help us to simplify things. But in that powerful usefulness also lies their trouble.

The thing with metrics and numerical goals is that we are quick to overvalue them and that our minds replace the real goal (for example improved safety) with its numerical expression on the management dashboard (for example a reduced number of incidents). This is a typical effect of Kahneman's *System 1* taking control and replacing a difficult problem with a much easier, but seemingly similar, problem[15]. The problem, of course, is that the two problems may be related and appear to be the same thing to our quick and superficial thinking, but they are not. And in fact, almost all (or probably all) metrics are merely a flawed approximation of what we are really after. Just think of the various ways to look at safety, and not one metric covering all of it!

The weaker the link between metric and the real underlying goal, the more problematic this replacement becomes. So before installing some metric, you need to think about ways how you intend to reach your underlying goal and connect these ways to your metrics. And even when you do so, you will need to check continuously that your metric is not manipulated (intentionally or unintentionally).

Continuous critical monitoring is one (reactive) way to counter some of the side effects of measurement. Another reactive countermeasure is to de-couple metrics and incentives[16] (rewards). A proactive approach to reduce these harmful effects is by involving people (respect their expertise!) in the questions of how we can reach our goals, and how we should measure our progress. Not only will this give frontliners understanding of what you are trying to achieve, it also gives them ownership, and most likely they will come up with the better and more practical approaches - approaches that more often than not will lead to win-win situations that improve several factors at once. Most likely, involvement will also lead to a more varied look at the matter, and to more than one way to 'measure'.

[1] This is an enhanced version of Myth 69 from *Safety Myth 101*.

[2] Usually attributed to management guru Peter Drucker, but probably not the origin of the slogan (there used to be an article about it on www.druckerinstitute.com, but it appears to be gone). Lord Kelvin would make an earlier candidate. Do under no circumstances ever attribute it to W. Edwards Deming - just read on!

[3] For a quick version, check: https://en.wikipedia.org/wiki/New_public_management (checked 18 July 2019)

[4] Deming said in the 2000 edition of his book *The New Economics*: "It is wrong to suppose that if you can't measure it, you can't manage it – a costly myth."

Deming, W.E. (2000) *The New Economics for Industry, Government, Education - 2nd Edition*. Cambridge, MA: MIT Press.

[5] We talk about the Hawthorne effect when people alter their behaviour or reaction in response to their awareness of being observed, and not necessarily because of other variables that have been changed. This means that conclusions about the relationships between variables can be compromised.

[6] Hopkins, A. & Maslen, S. (2015) *Risky Rewards: How Company Bonuses Affect Safety*. Farnham: Ashgate.

[7] I was in an interesting episode when working on the annual statistics for the Norwegian Rail Administration. There was this statistics advisor whom I told that things should not be taken that seriously and that we should not spend hours of work to clear up a difference of 10 level crossings between two reports (one compiled by us, the other by the regulator). The smart way to deal with it would be to fake it and just adjust ours to the regulator's or vice versa. She was quite annoyed because 10 was a pretty major difference! I begged to differ on a total of nearly 4.000 and added that this was no exact science. She exploded. Of course mathematics was an exact science! Yes, I replied, but we were not dealing with mathematics. We were running a business and you do not need exact numbers for that, especially if it will cost you disproportional resources to get the exact numbers. As far as I was concerned roughly right should be more than enough.

[8] Check the chapter titled *Intervention, NOW!* later in this book.

[9] Just a random example: A fellow Safety Professional once told me,

> "At a recent project with a client I had to learn that the promotional program is a requirement for achieving a certain safety grading as it would account for quite a significant number of marks on the score sheet. The organisation allocates a substantial amount of funds to propagate and promote safety via this program which seemed to be, IMO, a waste of funds that could have been spent more productively".

This sounds to me like a perfect example where the tool became a goal in itself. Twice over actually. One might think that the purpose of a safety system is to make things safer. In this example the goal was apparently to be certified or get a high score. Likewise the promotional program should aim at making things safer, but the incentive for the company was the number of points.

[10] Even though the numbers will be wrong, there is under-reporting, and so on. Yes. The numbers are 'wrong' and they always will be. And they are everywhere else too. Get over it and do not use it as an excuse to do nothing. Only because they are incomplete that does not mean that you cannot use them. Just do not believe that they are the truth, the whole truth and nothing but the truth.

[11] There is an interesting parallel here to the discussion about quantitative and qualitative risk assessments. If you want to follow up on this thought, please check the final chapter about *Risk* in *Safety Myth 101*. Or wait for a new book about that subject…

[12] Since there tends to be a major focus on budgets and costs we run into another problem with numbers. It is quite easy to specify the costs of training (costs of the course, production, hours lost to training, etc.), but impossible to express the benefit from training in gains, or avoided losses. Costs are visible to bean counters, benefits not so much. This does not only apply to training, but most safety actions.

[13] Although it seems that William Bruce Cameron is the more correct choice: https://quoteinvestigator.com/2010/05/26/everything-counts-einstein/ (checked 15 July 2019).

It is a recommendable practice to follow up and double check quotes and not be misled by internet memes. If you can, find and read primary sources and quote them. It is a lot of effort, of course, but better than making a fancy statement that in fact makes you look silly. Alternatively, add a qualifier. Like I did. "Commonly attributed to" is a rather smart choice…

[14] This section is a.o. inspired by the HBR article about the Wells Fargo scandal, and similar occasions when "strategy is being hijacked by numbers".

Harris, M. & Tayler, B. (2019) Don't Let Metrics Undermine Your Business. *Harvard Business Review*, September/October 2019. Retrieved 1 September 2019 from https://hbr.org/2019/09/dont-let-metrics-undermine-your-business

Additionally, it seems that Deming has said repeatedly that there could be nothing worse than goals without method…

[15] You will encounter this several times through this book. Here is the source:

Kahneman, D. (2011) *Thinking Fast And Slow*. New York: Farrar, Straus and Giroux.

[16] Check the chapter on incentive schemes later in this book.

Constructs

-Constructs--Causation--Objectivity-

A main source of many misunderstandings and misapplications of measurement is the measurement of constructs. One main problem with measuring constructs is that they are not 'real' things (objects) to be found in the natural world, ready to be observed by you and measured by some kind of objective way of measurement. Unlike a chair or a rock, you will not find a construct in the physical world, even though we use them to describe and explain observations and mechanisms in the physical world.

Early mythology and ancient beliefs are filled with constructs, one could say. To explain the noise during thunderstorms, our ancestors made up gods of thunder, like Thor who hit something with his hammer Mjolnir, causing the thunder. Even though science and society have progressed since then, there may be even more constructs in today's world and in our everyday use than ever before. This may even be caused by this very progress.

A construct is a product of our mind (or minds, it can be a social process) to make sense of something or as a help to explain something. An example of a construct from physics would be the centre of mass. We can calculate and determine where it 'is', but when we look there, it is not really a thing. In several cases it is even so that there is nothing but air in the location where you have determined the centre of mass...

Constructs are even more common in the social sciences, like in psychology (e.g. intelligence), in sociology (e.g. culture), and also in safety. Actually, many 'things' in safety are constructs[1] (and thus not really 'things' at all). Just think of risk, causes, safety culture, errors, unsafe acts, accidents, SIF[2], resilience, and... safety itself! This means that any attempt of measuring one of these things often results in an attempt to measure the unmeasurable. The results may not necessarily be useless, but they are no hard science, no truth in themselves, they are at best one particular way of looking at something and that may, or may not, be helpful in improving the situation - or serve other purposes, like control. Or selling consultancy hours.

Let us look at an example[3].

A friend of mine attended a conference and sent me a picture of a presentation. It looked something like the chart below.

Relative impact of factors on origin of accidents

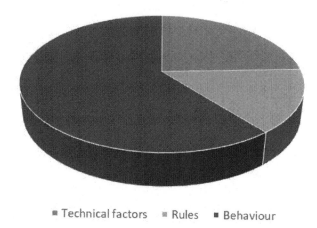

■ Technical factors   ■ Rules   ■ Behaviour

There had been some 'research' among safety practitioners and the results of the online questionnaire survey showed a distribution of impact factors ('causes') on the origin of accidents. Similar charts have been around since the dawn of times (the most famous probably Heinrich's 88:10:2 ratio[4]). There are two main problems with them:

1. Causes are constructs.
2. Because they are, counting them and presenting them in statistics like this is meaningless or worse.

As explained above, constructs are products of our mind. We use them to explain something, to make sense of something. Constructs are extremely useful. But they are not real things. They do not exist outside our minds. You cannot find a cause as such outside in the real world. And that is an interesting thought, because many of us will have been taught in the past that the objective of incident investigation is to *find* causes. Well, tough luck. Mission impossible. We make observations and then we decide in our heads what we call a cause. Often this is something that happened before the event we are reviewing.

Imagine I take a sheet of paper, crumble the sheet in my hand, make a ball of it and then drop the ball. What caused the ball to fall? Most will say that opening my hand and letting go caused the ball to fall. We see an effect, we observe what happened before, and then we choose a cause. So causes are things (acts or conditions) we choose. This may look quite simple and unproblematic, because what is the harm? And for most everyday situations this serves us well. Things get trickier when we try to categorize causes for statistical purposes. Let us take another really simple example to illustrate.

You have surely heard about Pompeii. 2000 years ago it was a prospering city in the southern part of Italy. And then one day it was not. What caused that disaster to happen? Surely the volcano, you will say. And yes, it was the lava and ash erupting and flowing from the Mount Vesuvius that covered the city and killed thousands. But on the other hand - many other volcanos erupt around the world without consequences like these. So we need something else to explain the fatalities, like the decision of people to live there. And they probably did with a good reason, for example because the area was fertile. So what caused the disaster? Was it the eruption of the volcano? Or the decision to live there? Or both? And maybe something else in addition? We choose what story to tell. Even restricting to only two factors (volcano and a decision) gives us three different possibilities!

And it is the same with that ball of paper. Does it fall because I let go - something you can observe. Or does it fall because of gravity - something you have learned is there? Or is all this happening because I just have to demonstrate a point to you and make up this silly experiment? There is no cause here hanging in the air for you to find. You decide, you construct a cause based on your knowledge and your choices about what you are going to mention. This makes the process of causation pretty subjective[5].

So, back to point two, why should you not count causes? Well, as we saw, since they are constructs, and thus figments of you mind, you can shape them anyway you want and get any number you want. Also, you will be unable to compare them reliably to other people's perception. Whenever people present you with causes and numbers, be very cautious. In most cases they are probably nonsense, even when they are delivered with a pretence of research.

And what is the problem with that? One big problem is that they most likely misdirect your efforts. Taking the pie chart from the previous page, it may suggest that the biggest problem is behaviour and that we need to direct our efforts there. However, that would ignore what the reasons for that behaviour are and these may rather be problems on an organisational level (e.g. work pressure or conflicting objectives) or environmental (e.g. situations that 'trick' people into certain behaviour).

Therefore an awareness and understanding of constructs is quite important in safety (and other areas) and one of the major eye openers from the past few years for me personally. Most of the concepts we use are actually constructs. They are not real things that exist in the physical world. They are figments of our mind that help us to make sense of the world and to solve problems. But that also means that their use can lead to confusion, and misuse or abuse. And this is quite essential in many discussions.

One of the problems with many constructs is that even though they are not 'real things', people tend to 'reify' them and treat them as a 'thing'. As something that you can observe and measure, and count objectively. Ironically, those perceptions and beliefs are much easier to 'sell' than uncertain notions of cause or culture as a social construct. It is much easier to have a scale you measure a construct against and then act as if it actually means something… And ignoring who draws the line and what the line is based on.

These examples of causes as constructs serve as an illustration for other constructs within safety where we try to measure and then attach much more meaning to the results of our 'measurement' than we should. By all means, pretending that something (a construct) can be measured can be a very useful approach, because it gives you something to discuss and a way to think about possible improvements. However, it is important to stay humble about these measurements. Keep in mind that they are merely an imperfect means to an end and that they have not that much substance - even though they may look impressive.

###

---

[1] If you want to read a truly mind blowing (and, admittedly difficult) paper on the subject, try:

Le Coze, J-C. (2012) Towards a Constructivist Program in Safety. *Safety Science*, 50: 1873–1887. doi:10.1016/j.ssci.2012.03.019.

[2] SIF = serious injury and fatality. We will get to these later in the book.

[3] There is a YouTube version of this section, check it at: https://www.youtube.com/watch?v=wzMBtgLrbbA

[4] Heinrich, H.W. (1941) *Industrial Accident Prevention (second edition)*. New York: McGraw-Hill.

[5] Another clear example of causes as being constructs is the fundamental attribution error. If you perform an activity and things go wrong, you are very much inclined to blame this on others or external circumstances. If someone else does the same and it goes wrong, you will be much more inclined to blame the person in question for his or her carelessness, incompetence and so on. The same happens when things go right. Here we see that different causes are chosen, or constructed, for the same event depending on who it happens to or who is involved.

Ross, L. (1977) The Intuitive Psychologist and his Shortcomings: Distortions in the Attribution Process. In: Berkowitz, L. (ed.). *Advances in Experimental Social Psychology*. New York: Academic Press: 173-220.

Jones, E.E. & Harris, V.A. (1967) The Attribution of Attitudes. *Journal of Experimental Social Psychology*, 3 (1): 1- 24. doi: 10.1016/0022-1031(67)90034-0.

Zero S.M.A.R.T.[1]

Many people argue that the only real goal for safety can be 'Zero', which comes in various guises, including "Zero Fatalities", "Zero Injuries" or "Zero Accidents", "Zero Harm" and of course there is the world-wide "Vision Zero"[2] campaign. I have even heard about a safety program called NiNa - "No Incidents No Accidents". And it appears to make sense intuitively; after all, we do not want anyone to die on their job, or as a result of our activities, or do we?

So, "Zero Accidents" does have a certain appeal, but do you remember the start of the book where we concluded that absence of accidents was not the same as presence of safety?[3] And earlier in this book, we also saw that outcome indicators like fatalities, injuries and accidents make for bad indicators and goals. But the problems with "Zero Harm" run deeper than that.

The first thing we might ask ourselves when we want to see "Zero Accidents" as a goal is if "Zero Accidents" does follow the SMART criteria. After all, goals should. SMART stands for:

S	=	Specific
M	=	Measurable
A	=	Acceptable[4]
R	=	Realistic
T	=	Timebound

A "Zero Accidents" goal complies with many of the SMART criteria. It is very *Specific* (Zero is pretty much as specific as things get) and *Measurable* (easy, just count[5]), it may be *Accepted* (which depends upon your organisation) and it can be *Timebound* (e.g. by giving a period, like 'this year'). The problem, however, is that "Zero Accidents" as a goal is not *Realistic*.

Unless you make a number of incorrect/unrealistic assumptions, of course. Zero builds on the premises that "All Accidents Are Preventable"[6]. However, not all accidents are preventable. They are only preventable if we have full control, full foresight and unlimited resources. Since we have neither of these (after all, we are living in a messy, uncertain world and have to do with limited knowledge, time and resources) not all accidents are preventable, and therefore Zero cannot be realistic.

Sure, you may reach it for a short time, or for a longer period of time even. You may recall that the Deep Water Horizon managed seven years without an LTI and even had a celebration for this the day before the accident happened. Actually, if you manage to reach Zero for a while this may give people a wrong focus because it suggests that things are safe when there are no accidents and that may not be the case - no accidents may happen just because of sheer luck.

Another problem with "Zero Harm" goals is that they usually only include safety goals. The main problems for workers may not be in safety, but rather related to occupational health. Long lasting effects of exposure to harmful chemicals, biological agents, physical or psychological stress or at least when looking at long term effects and death toll[7].

Zero goals are frustrating goals. After all, the Zero goal is an absolute that strives for perfection and therefore it only needs a tiny mishap to fail. If it fails, then you will get a 'red' score on your scorecard for the remainder of the year that you cannot do anything about. This does not motivate, since the score is ruined already. And what use is it to make an effort? This leads us to the next problem, namely that Zero goals invite to bending definitions and categories, gaming the system or downright cheating.

A great source for arguments against "Zero Harm" is Robert Long's[8] work. He stresses among other things that Zero requires perfection. Perfectionism has positive sides as it can motivate individuals to achieve goals, but can also be a destructive thing and is actually a psychological disorder. Not really something that one should want to seek out… Gavin Nascimento seems to have said: "Making mistakes leads to progress. Faking perfection leads to unhappiness. Choose wisely".

The call for Zero and perfection can be very oppressive, for example when it is elevated as part of an organisation's Safety Policy. This communication of absolutes may then block out more nuanced and realistic views and become ideology instead of critical thinking, causing the suppression of 'bad' news and having adverse effects on learning. It may lead to wilful ignorance.

"Zero Harm" is about control. It does not allow for error and thereby it inhibits learning. As painful and tragic for the people involved as it sometimes may be, trial and error, sometimes with bad consequences, is essential for learning and improvement. "Zero Harm" does not allow for this.

Those who feel that "Zero Harm" is the only morally acceptable 'goal' should keep in mind that we do not need to have any goals for accidents at all. Let us find other, better, performance indicators instead and monitor incidents and accidents just for statistics and as an indicator, not as a goal or objective.

Pursuing a Zero Goal may see you hitting the target but missing the point!

p.s. 1. For the record, I am not against striving for zero accidents, or having a "Zero Accident Vision", but it must never become a goal. There is a massive difference between a vision ("I have a dream") and a goal (which is supposed to be concrete and SMART).

p.s. 2. And please do not fall for the common fallacy of asking "If our goal cannot be Zero, what number should we pick then?"[9] It is a sign of unconstructive binary thinking that shuts down creativity. It is not necessary at all to set goals for the number of accidents or their consequences. Rather think of goals that create safety, not quasi-goals that indicate the absence of safety.

p.s. 3. What if "Zero Harm" is preached but the behaviour shown is not in line with the words? As we saw before, when we discussed slogans, hollow words cause cynicism and destroy belief in safety programs - even the parts that are realistic and useful.

###

---

[1] Based on Myth 73 from *Safety Myth 101*.

[2] http://visionzero.global/ (checked 19 July 2019)

[3] Dave Collins has on several occasions commented in Linkedin discussions on the subject of 'Zero' that "Saying safety is zero harm is like saying love is zero hate". Brilliant.

Robert Long followed up on this with a blog post: https://safetyrisk.net/love-doesnt-set-targets/ (checked 21 July 2019)

[4] Depending upon your source the definition of the letters may vary slightly, but the general meaning is as I wrote it down here. Most variation is actually found around the 'A' which I have also seen as 'Agreed', 'Achievable', 'Attractive' or 'Ambitious'. Check Wikipedia and find more, 'Action-oriented' even!

[5] Although you may be fooling yourself, or be fooled by others. For example because your very measurement is an incentive to report differently...

[6] One of Safety's best known and most abused slogans.

[7] See the chapter *Zero Harm: Occupational Disease* elsewhere in this book.

[8] Check the second chapter of *Risk Makes Sense*, by Robert and Joshua Long and the second book *For The Love Of Zero*, by. Robert Long. Another great source is *From Accidents To Zero* by Andrew Sharman, especially the finally chapter on 'Zero'.

Long, R. & Long, J. (2012) *Risk Makes Sense: Human Judgement and Risk (2nd edition)*. Kambah, ACT: Scotoma Press.

Long, R. (2012) *For The Love of Zero: Human Fallibility and Risk*. Kambah, ACT: Scotoma Press.

Sharman, A. (2014) *From Accidents To Zero. A Practical Guide to Improving Your Workplace Safety Culture*. Maverick Eagle Press.

[9] Implicitly assuming that you are actually setting out to hurt people - check the applicable chapter elsewhere in this book!

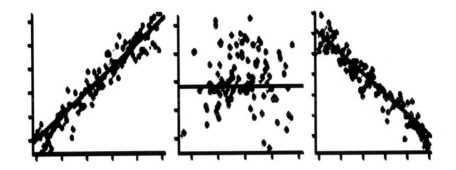

Correlation or Causation?[1]

-Statistics- -Causation- -Correlation-

As a true science and/or safety nerd, it is a joy to work together with like-minded spirits. So, one day, in order to explain to one of our colleagues the differences between correlation and causation, we devised a little experiment in the Bluewater HSEQ Department. After about five minutes of research, data collection and measurement we found the following:

Who	Height	Meetings
Person 1	1,85	4
Person 2	1,75	2
Person 3	1,7	1
Person 4	1,95	4
Person 5	1,85	3

Plotted in a graph[2], this provides an almost straight line and suggests a clear linear relationship between a person's height and the number of meetings this person has. The larger a person, the more meetings a day this person can expect.

Most readers will frown by now, a few will even reject this kind of nonsense right away. And still, look at that graph and experience how seductive it is. There is a perfect pattern[3], and we react to this like we react to clouds and ink blobs: we try to discover something in them[4]. This pattern we see must have a cause and a meaning. We just want to believe that this is so, and our first reaction is thinking into that line and even trying to find reasons why this is true.

If you think that this is absurd, just open a newspaper[5]. On almost any day, you will be able find stories in the media saying that "Science has discovered that…" After this follows usually some (perceived) connection between an activity, environmental factor, chemical compound or food type and people's health, well-being, intelligence, or fatality rate. One of my favourite examples, used often to illustrate the difference between causation and correlation, sees the highest number of drownings when the sales of ice cream are on their highest. Combine these two facts in a causal way and you may come to believe that eating ice cream is dangerous[6].

Of course this kind of reasoning forgets the uniting link of eating ice cream and going for a swim: hot summer weather. Even between hot summer weather and drowning there is not necessarily a causal connection. All you have is a very strong correlation. When talking about causes, things like swimming too far from the shore, hypothermia, being caught by an underwater stream or the tide are much more likely candidates. We should probably regard the hot summer weather as context rather than as a cause[7].

Also in safety causation and correlation are often mixed up. This is especially evident in the many instances that statistical evidence is quoted to prove one point or another. Causation means indeed correlation, because cause and effect *do* happen together. It is important to understand that the opposite is *not* true. Correlation does *not* prove causation, not even when there is a very high correlation. Or to say otherwise - correlation alone is not enough. And to take things one step further, a known effect happening does not mean that a known cause 'did it'. Quoting my friend Alan Quilley:

> "Just because there are gifts under the tree on Christmas morning, does not mean Santa is real".

---

[1] This chapter is a reworked and enhanced version of Myth 17 from *Safety Myth 101*.

[2] Which looks like this:

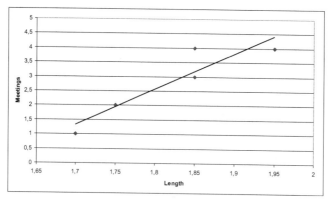

[3] These 'patterns' can be easily tricked through a number of graphical manipulations or sleights of hand. You will find a chapter with some of the most common tricks later on in this book.

[4] A nice blog on the subject: https://towardsdatascience.com/your-dataset-is-a-giant-inkblot-test-b9bf4c53eec5 (checked 19 July 2019)

[5] And I dare to bet that your organisation's annual report may be another useful source... Sorry!

[6] Especially when going for a swim. Most likely your mom told you about not eating before swimming, although probably not referring to 'statistics' like this.

[7] A great source of nonsense correlations (and excellent examples to make the point) is found in the work of Tyler Vigen who even wrote a book on the subject, titled *Spurious Correlations*. A quick introduction is possible through the short article in *Harvard Business Report* (https://hbr.org/2015/06/beware-spurious-correlations) or check out Vigen's website, which provides hours of fun with statistics: http://tylervigen.com/spurious-correlations

Injury Rates Tell How Well You Do[1]

Injury rates are the traditional and most widely accepted and practiced means to measure safety. Look up any safety statistics (governmental, or for companies) and you will mainly find this kind of lagging indicators: number of fatalities, number of injuries, and LTI[2] rates. Since everybody is doing this and because regulations ask for these things to be reported. Besides, they are easy to understand, so this surely must be a good way of measuring safety?

Measuring safety by accidents is rooted in the widespread belief that safety is defined by absence of accidents[3]. Following this logic, the lower the number of fatalities or injuries the better our safety results. Or are they?

It is surely desirable that low injury rates are a result of good safety management. It is reasonable to expect that companies that do a great job on safety management will have few accidents. But we cannot simply turn the argument around and say because there is a low number of reported injuries, the company has managed safety well. After all, there are many other ways to get low numbers, including dumb luck, stretching definitions, under-reporting, not reporting at all, and even gaming the injury rates.

Much of this reasoning of injury rates as a measure for safety, boils down to the phenomenon of System 1 and System 2 thinking as described by Daniel Kahneman[4]. I am in particular thinking of substituting a difficult question with a simpler question. The question "Are we good at safety management?" is a difficult and complex question. So our brains try to find an easier to answer question that seemingly covers the same subject. When we define 'safety' as 'absence of accidents', it is easy to assume that 'good safety management' is the same as 'low number of injuries'. And there you go…

Another problem is the question in how far you can manage consequences of accidents. Certainly one can do so to a certain degree by establishing barriers. Much of the common personal protective equipment has exactly that goal, as do seatbelts and airbags.

One should realise, however, that the difference between a serious injury and just a scratch is often only a matter of inches, which means in many cases coincidence, randomness and sheer good or bad luck. Often it is as banal as being at the right/wrong place at the right/wrong time.

One accident can have widely different outcomes that lie way outside the control of an organisation. Take for example a collision of a train with a car on a level crossing without automatic barriers. In one case, this may concern a middle-aged man driving to work alone. He is in a hurry because he has an important meeting in half an hour and so he takes the chance of crossing the level crossing even though the warning signals are on. He does not make it, the car is hit by a passing freight train and he dies. In an alternative scenario there is a mother with a minivan, driving her own kids and their friends to football practice. She is late and also decides to take the chance of driving over the level crossing despite the active warning signals. Also this car is hit, only now the outcome is five fatalities.

The accident in both examples was the same, but the consequences of the second example were much more severe. What does that teach us? In this scenario, the train company or infrastructure manager could have prevented (or at least reduced the likelihood of) the accident for example by installing protective barriers in addition to warning lights[5], but they have no possibility to control the outcome of an accident when it happens.

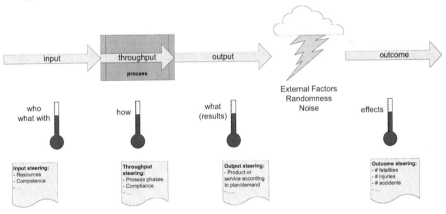

This has led me to think in terms of consequences of things that we can affect (output from our processes) and things that we have little control over (which I like to call outcomes[6]). If we then draw a simplified process model, like the one above, we can see that we have a process where we have some input, certain activities within the process and a product/output. But it does not stop there. At the end, we have those things connected to our processes that we have little control over; the outcomes. In all of these 'phases' (input, throughput, output and outcome) we can do quantitative or qualitative measurements and collect information that we can or cannot use to manage our processes[7].

One thing that the simplified process model also illustrates very well: to have good information about how well our process is functioning, it is probably wise to get the information as close to the process as possible. With that in mind, it is strange that we often choose metrics that are actually furthest away from the process - like injuries and fatalities. These say extremely little about what we do, so they are not very useful to serve as a judge of our safety management activities.

An additional problem is that accidents leading to fatalities and injuries are what are called "rare events" because of the elements of chance and probability involved. Infrequent and unpredictable occurrence make them unsuitable as indicators to say how well we are doing on safety. This is by no means a novel insight - check for example a paper by Jacobs from 1970[8].

So far, we have looked at the meaninglessness of injury rates as a safety indicator from a somewhat theoretical point of view. There are other ways to build a critique of injury rates. An interesting approach followed by Marloes Nitert and Sidney Dekker, is to look at the issue from a statistical point of view and determine whether changes in injury numbers are statistically significant at all. An example, discussed on the Safety Differently website[9] illustrates that most common results are not. Even though there appears to be a major reduction in absolute numbers, due to the often limited size of the population or exposure, these changes (positive and negative, by the way) are most likely by chance, or natural fluctuations rather than that they are a consequence of your action or inaction[10].

---

[1] Based on Myth 71 from *Safety Myth 101*.

[2] LTI = Lost Time Injury

[3] See the second chapter in this book (*Measuring what?*) where we discussed a number of ways to define safety. Absence of accidents was one of them.

[4] If you have not read Daniel Kahneman's great book then now is probably a good time:

Kahneman, D. (2011) *Thinking Fast And Slow*. New York: Farrar, Straus and Giroux.

[5] There may be good reasons why this was not the case. Safety management requires making decisions where to spend money and where not. And do keep in mind that absence of barriers not automatically equals cause for an accident. There is also the issue of counterfactual reasoning. This means that one assumes that everything that could have prevented an accident is a cause. It is thinking that if something is a 'cure' for something the lack of this must be a cause. That would make lack of aspirin make a cause of headaches, go figure! Counterfactual reasoning is often characterised by thinking in terms of "If only…", and verbs like "should". A good discussion and explanation of counterfactual reasoning can be found in Hollnagel's book *Barriers And Accident Prevention*, see a.o. page 31:

Hollnagel, E. (2004) *Barriers And Accident Prevention*. Aldershot: Ashgate.

6 Sidney Dekker and others talk about dependent and independent variables which is also a very good way of thinking about these things. Check for example the following blog:

https://www.safetydifferently.com/zero-pessimism/ (checked 14 October 2019)

7 Eric Arne Lofquist has written a very nice paper on the subject of measuring safety. Here he uses a more or less similar model in which he distinguishes between proactive measures (which deal with the system's design), interactive measures (dealing with system operations) and reactive measures (which are about system outcomes).

Lofquist, E.A. (2010) The Art of Measuring Nothing: The Paradox of Measuring Safety in a Changing Civil Aviation Industry using Traditional Safety Metrics. *Safety Science*, 48: 1520-1529. doi: 10.1016/j.ssci.2010.05.006.

8 Jacobs, H. H. (1970) Towards more Effective Safety Measurement Systems. *Journal of Safety Research*, 2: 160-175.

9 Nitert, M. & Dekker, S.W.A. (2019) *When Does A Reduction In Injury Numbers Become Statistically Significant?* Retrieved 21 July 2019 from www.safetydifferently.com/when-does-a-reduction-in-injury-numbers-become-statistically-significant/

The article contained at time of writing some (minor) mistakes, and is open for some critique, but it is a good example of how one could appraise the issue critically (and scientifically) and invites at the least to a much more humble view of improved injury rates.

10 You may be surprised to see that a very similar argument as Nitert and Dekker make already was found about 30 years earlier in a handbook on Behaviour Based Safety! Check pages 41-46, and 85 in:

Krause, T.R., Hidley, J.H. & Hodson, S.J. (1990) *The Behavior-Based Process. Managing Involvement for an Injury-Free Culture*. New York: Van Nostrand-Reinhold.

The text says among other things, "…the injury frequency rate is a measure that is accumulating validity as time goes by, but these frequencies are of no predictive value to safety management on a monthly or even quarterly basis." because "…very large number of hours worked must be logged before this method of measurement achieves statistical validity." Concluding rather strong: "…given the misplaced trust that people accord to frequency rates, these numbers are an outright hindrance to proactive safety management." (all quotes from p.43)

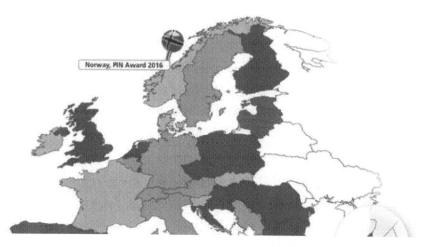

Norway, PIN Award 2016

Surrogates or the Real Deal?[1]

-Statistics- -Indicators- -Surrogate-

Reading Ben Goldacre's "statistics toilet book"[2], I came across the term "Surrogate Outcomes". Goldacre discusses this in a health (and general science) context, but they are also super relevant for safety - and other business objectives.

Surrogate Outcomes are when you measure something other than what you really are interested in because you have a hard time measuring one thing and you know or assume that the other thing is correlated to it. Based on your measurements, you draw conclusions about the first thing. I had heard the term before, but this time it struck a note and I decided to look a bit deeper into the subject.

Surrogate Outcomes

In clinical trials, a Surrogate Outcome (or Surrogate Marker[3]) is a measure of effect of a specific treatment that may correlate with a real clinical endpoint, but does not necessarily have a guaranteed relationship. Based on the measurements, we draw a conclusion about what we actually are interested in. Surrogate Outcomes are used when the primary endpoint is undesired (like for example death), it is unethical to devise an experiment which measures the outcome directly (again, for example pain or death) or when the number of events is very small, thus making it impractical to conduct a clinical trial to gather a statistically significant number of endpoints.

One known example to illustrate Surrogate Outcomes is cholesterol. It is known that higher cholesterol levels increase the likelihood for heart disease, but the relationship is not linear. Many people with normal cholesterol levels develop a heart disease, while many others with high cholesterol do not. The primary endpoint in this case is "Death from heart disease", but "cholesterol level" is used as the Surrogate Outcome. A clinical trial may show that a particular drug is effective in reducing cholesterol, without showing directly that it prevents fatalities.

Because we have problems to measure Safety directly (huge problems, in fact), we use quite a lot of Surrogate Outcomes to measure our efforts. Toxicity of substances is an example. We cannot test this directly on humans for quite obvious reasons, so it is tested on 'similar' organisms, like rats. Leaving the irony of that comparison for what it is, we can reflect on some problems. Because although rats are mammals, like humans, there are some serious differences (like weight and size), and there is no guarantee that we indeed react the same way. For this reason in general, a safety factor is added to the test results. This makes the surrogate marker an approximation, but one that tends to be sufficient for our purposes.

Somewhat confusingly, maybe, after reading the general explanation above: one of the commonly used surrogate markers for safety is the number of fatalities. Let us have a look at a real life example to see how this works and what pitfalls we may encounter.

The Case

The first version of this chapter was conceived after a news report on our intranet caught my attention. It was about the Road Safety PIN Award 2016[4] for Outstanding Progress in Road Safety[5], awarded to Norway by the European Transport Safety Council (ETSC). The article echoed the press release[6] of the National Road Administration (Statens Vegvesen, SVV) that claimed that Norway was honoured with a European award for the safest roads in the world.

Let us be generous and not dwell on the obvious mistake in the title of SVV's press release, which is likely a slip of the pen of an overenthusiastic PR-consultant, extrapolating Europe to Global scale. Let us instead focus on other elements. Without having the possibility to go in-depth (road safety is a fairly complex, yet fascinating, subject that would require much more study), I would like to address some important points.

How to Measure Safety?

Now this is a difficult question, and one for that, at least to my knowledge, no one has managed to find a satisfactory solution. This does not stop people pretending that they can, and so we find a wide selection of statistics everywhere. The most common way is of course counting the number of fatalities or injuries. Ignoring for the moment the dilemma whether one should measure something by its absence, I think that the biggest problem lies in the certainty with which some people conclude that absence of accidents (or negative outcomes) means that something is safe.

That is clearly a logical fallacy. It is a basic ground rule in safety (but one that is little understood and practiced by professionals, politicians and the public alike) that while the occurrence of accidents can[7] mean that there are problems with regard to safety, the absence of accidents does NOT mean that things are safe. You can achieve the same, for example by pure chance, luck or under-reporting.

There is another major problem, namely the relative randomness of consequences like fatalities and injuries. Related to road safety, the difference between life and death, or between serious and light injuries may lie in things like what kind of traffic participant you are, the type of car, speed, the angle in which you are hit, and obviously the number of people involved in the accident. A much better indicator for safety than the number of outcomes would be the number of accidents (e.g. collisions). We cannot tell from the data, but maybe there are just as many accidents in Norway as in previous years and it is just through some of the aforementioned factors that fewer people die?

It is hard for organisations like ETCS to get good data. The ETCS bases her report on numbers of fatalities (and serious injuries) that each country reports. They encounter very much all of the problems above, and then some. Even though I doubt that many fatal accidents will go unreported, some countries have shaky registrations and routines, some only register certain accidents, and definitions of what a serious injury is differ from country to country. Information about the number of accidents seems to be unavailable. I tried to find them for Norway, but I fear that this information is spread over many players, including the Police, SVV, municipalities, insurance companies (even Statistics Norway[8] does not have the info, I checked) and the minor things go probably entirely unreported.

Toying with Relatives

What I often find problematic, is how reports like this toy around with relative numbers. Even though I often prefer relative numbers to absolute numbers, they can also contribute to confusion or paint a more positive (or negative for that matter) picture than you would. Be wary when you are presented with a series of percentages that all serve to support a certain point of view. As Gerd Gigerenzer[9] has taught us, we have always to ask "percentage of what?". And just check if you are suspicious.

I am not saying that the ETCS has done something obviously wrong, when they first write that there was a 44% decrease between 2010 and 2015 and then continue with "an impressive 20% drop in 2015 compared to 2014 levels". It is just a bit redundant or unclear what they want to say. Most likely, they are trying to stress the good news. That message can be constructed in a number of ways, however. Look at the statistics and you can calculate that there was a 20% reduction in 2015 compared to 2012 levels as well.

As we saw, outcomes can be seemingly random and fickle. They can just as well go up again. The Norwegian minister of traffic acknowledges this. He is pleased about the praise from ETCS saying that "the best reductions were reached in Norway, where the number of road deaths decreased by 20%...", but appears to be better briefed than the Council. "The number of accidents on Norwegian roads will vary due to randomness from year to year", he said.

Indeed, the 20% reduction may sound like a lot, but from 2012 to 2013, there was an increase of over 40 fatalities (29%, just to confuse you further with percentages). Easy come, easy go. In situations where the variation can be so large, flinging around relative numbers compared to the previous year has little or no value and one should rather observe long-term trends. Still, this practice is very common in many safety reports.

More Surrogate Markers

I do not know how the concept of leading and lagging indicators goes together with Surrogate Markers, but let us just try and maybe start a discussion. If I am entirely missing the point, please point this out to me!

Judging from the use in clinical trials, Surrogate Markers tend to be leading indicators: lower cholesterol should lead to lower chance of heart disease. Fatalities, however, or accidents are clearly a Lagging Surrogate Marker for Road Safety. Apparently, the ETSC also uses Leading Surrogate Markers. Their press release states that,

> "Declines in the level of police enforcement of traffic offences are contributing to Europe's failure to cut the numbers dying in road collisions", and continues "In a separate report on enforcement, ETSC found that, in over half the countries where data is available, the number of tickets issued over the last five years for use of a mobile phone while driving has reduced, suggesting lower levels of enforcement across Europe"[10].

In this case enforcement is seen as a Surrogate Marker for Safety (defined as 'fewer fatalities') because it is assumed that more enforcement leads to better compliance with traffic safety regulations, leads to fewer accidents, leads to fewer fatalities and better safety. This reasoning makes intuitive sense to many people, but is not without problems because things are not always that linear. More enforcement can also lead to a greater deal of keeping up appearances and after the control post is passed, people speed up just an extra bit to make up for 'lost time'.

There are other problems. The press release tells us: "Sweden, The Netherlands and Finland are among countries that have reported falls in speeding tickets issued". I do recall that several years ago the Dutch Police Force (and without any doubt Police in other countries too) had specific numerical goals for the number of speeding tickets per year. I do not know if they still have, but abolishing these ridiculous goals will probably lead to a different focus (most likely whatever new political goal they got). Speaking of focus, complaining about reduced traffic enforcement, clearly ignores other priorities that might just have been a bit more important for society at the very moment of writing - like terror attacks and dealing with the largest wave of fugitives in Europe since Attila the Hun.

Besides, speeding tickets are nothing but a Surrogate Marker, because it is assumed that they say something about speeding behaviour. Of course, there are other possible reasons for fewer speeding tickets, like better general compliance of speed limits (not that I seriously believe that this is the case, but hypothetically speaking). Interestingly, this one is also a marker that tries to measure something (traffic safety, or rather, compliance) by its absence...

Like it or not, unless someone comes up with a brilliant way to measure safety as the 'real deal', we will have to work with Surrogate Outcomes for the time being (and all of the foreseeable future). This is okay as long as we understand the limitations and communicate within those limitations.

Where Is the Systems View?

There is one more comment that I must make. The cry for more enforcement is basically a claim that the system is safe if it were not for those stupid and non-compliant people in it. The title and the message from the press releases mentioned above also reflect this view. The SVV claims that the award is about "the safest roads" (not so strange, after all, that is what they are all about) while they probably should have talked about the traffic system as a whole.

Because, are the roads really so safe? Intuitively, I would say Danish roads are much safer than Norwegian ones. And compare the German Autobahn to motorways in Norway and you can count proper motorways almost on one hand (even though there is clearly improvement in recent years). Many Norwegian roads can be characterised as narrow, there are many tunnels (many of them also pretty narrow), the roads go through challenging landscapes, they are strongly affected by weather and seasons and do not underestimate the presence of rather large wild animals. Thinking of those, collisions with large animals like moose or reindeer rarely lead to fatal accidents (or serious injuries for people), but lead to major to damage and have a rather high potential. Although there are many of these accidents, I do not think they reflect in the ETCS numbers at all because they lack particular outcomes.

So, when talking safety on the roads, this might be in many cases thanks to the drivers (who adjust their speed to conditions and handle the constant variability in a rather good way) and not despite of the drivers. Another important factor is certainly the improving quality of cars, and the opportunity of many Norwegians to afford them.

It would be fun to do a proper study of all these factors, and I would not be very surprised if the findings would echo many of the remarks that John Adams already made in his brilliant book[11] almost 25 years ago. Adams also mentioned already an issue that was raised by SVV Director Guro Ranes: "We are concerned about the negative trend for seriously injured pedestrians and cyclists". Adams questioned the fact that there was a lot of attention for protecting the best-protected traffic participants (car drivers). This only lead to riskier behaviour, while there was little attention for the weaker parties (pedestrians and cyclists).

Safe or Not Safe?

Having made all these critical remarks, it must be said that there appears to be a steady decline in fatalities since the 1960s. Also, the number of (light and serious) injuries seems to have a steady decline. If you feel like it, you can download numbers from Statistics Norway[12] and play with them to check for yourself (as I did).

I cannot say what has led to this trend, but there has been a lot of good and serious work on road and traffic safety, so one can assume that from a variety of measures at least some have had positive effects. Has the traffic system become safer? We have some circumstantial evidence pointing that way, but I would hold back hallelujah-stories, because there are still many hazards and also worrying new ones, like for example a growing number of East European trucks in doubtful state, with unfit tyres, etc.

As an aside, doing a bit of research on the web I found an interesting British take on the matter[13], commenting that they were the second safest, but were "punished" for not making more progress from an already safe situation. Well, yet another argument to leave Europe…

A positive, yet critical, conclusion

One might wonder why some Safety People (among which yours truly) appear to be so grumpy. Can we not just be happy that there is a low number of fatal accidents? Should we not celebrate a low number of traffic fatalities? Yes, we should, because it is good news! However, should we also conclude that we are safest based on some outcome number? No! We just cannot tell without additional information, and a sensible definition of what safety means! So please learn to be reluctant to draw quick and easy conclusions, even if it these may be highly flattering.

Road traffic is a complex system where safety is created by (or emerges from) a large number of factors and their relationships. Do not give in to oversimplification (especially illogical forms), and whenever you see positive numbers also ask for the 'Bad News' and/or look for evidence that disproves a 'Good News' hypothesis. Confirmation can be (too) easy. Trying to falsify may be harder, but it will make your findings more robust and valuable!

Epilogue

And don't we hate it to be right… Only a week after I published my critical blog on which the above is based, it was announced[14] that already 16 people had lost their lives in that month (against 9 the same month the year before), and the national road administration was fearing a "Summer of Death" (their words, not mine). If you check their statistics[15], you can see how much these numbers fluctuate. The media seem not to be particularly concerned by this and so we see ever shifting news items[16]…

[1] This was originally a blog published in June 2016 to excellent response and some good discussions.

[2] Goldacre, B. (2014) *I Think You'll Find It's A Bit More Complicated Than That*. London: Fourth Estate.

[3] Get a rough introduction to the subject: https://en.wikipedia.org/wiki/Surrogate_endpoint (checked 21 July 2019)

[4] http://etsc.eu/10th-annual-road-safety-performance-index-pin-report/ (checked 21 July 2019)

[5] http://etsc.eu/20-june-2016-road-safety-performance-index-pin-conference/ (checked 21 July 2019)

[6] http://www.vegvesen.no/om+statens+vegvesen/presse/nyheter/Nasjonalt/norge-hedret-med-europeisk-trafikksikkerhetspris-for-verdens-tryggeste-veier (checked 21 July 2019)

[7] Mind you: can! Not: does!

[8] Knock yourself out at: https://www.ssb.no. There is also an English version of the site.

[9] Gigerenzer, G. (2014) *Risk Savvy. How to Make Good Decisions*. London: Allen Lane.

[10] http://etsc.eu/cuts-to-police-enforcement-across-europe-doubly-damaging-for-road-safety/ (checked 21 July 2019)

[11] Adams, J. (1995) *Risk*. Oxford: Routledge.

[12] Find the data here: https://www.ssb.no/statistikkbanken/selecttable/hovedtabellHjem.asp?KortNavnWeb=vtu&CMSSubjectArea=transport-og-reiseliv&checked=true (checked 21 July 2019)

[13] http://www.dailymail.co.uk/money/cars/article-3650973/Britain-second-safest-roads-Europe-European-Safety-Transport-Council-reveals.html (checked 21 July 2019)

[14] https://www.nrk.no/norge/vegvesenet-frykter-dodssommer-pa-veiene-1.13020457 (checked 20 July 2019).

[15] https://www.vegvesen.no/fag/Fokusomrader/Trafikksikkerhet/Ulykkesdata (checked 20 July 2019, and continuously updated).

[16] Or even a presentation (but not *realisation*) of the dilemma that accident numbers seemed to be heading towards a dramatic 'score' but suddenly there was the chance on the lowest fatality number in many decades:

https://www.nrk.no/sorlandet/faerre-drept-i-sommertrafikken-1.14643967 (checked 14 October 2019).

Who Are We Gonna Hurt Today?[1]

-Zero- -Goal- -Vision-

A goal, objective or target[2] is, simply put, something that you are trying to do or achieve. That sounds simple enough, but there are two main problems that we encounter quite often when it comes to goals in our organisations. Firstly, as discussed previously, there is a risk that a tool, which is the means to achieve the goal, quickly becomes a goal in its own right. Thereby it partly or entirely ruins the originally good idea - often without us noticing. Secondly, and the very thing I would address here is that goals are easily confused with visions or aspirations. This can also happen the other way around, when visions are mistakenly seen as goals. This happens for example when we obviously do not want anyone to be hurt and then declare this desire as a goal of 'zero harm'.

Throughout this book you will find many arguments against 'zero'. However logical these arguments may be, when one argues against 'Zero Goals' its defenders often counter with an argument that says that if you are not aiming for zero accidents, then by some twisted logic you want people to get hurt, or even worse, that you actually set out to hurt someone, in the line of "If our goal is not zero, who are we going to hurt then?", or "If the goal is not zero, what number should we pick then?".

I am getting sóóóóó tired of this argument. Really. I cannot even see how these people come to that conclusion. Must be some kind of binary "if you are not with us, then you are against us" type of argument. Little else makes sense. And not even that kind of black and white thinking makes remotely sense if you think just half a second about it logically.

Tell me, how many of us go out the door to do some shopping with the goal of not running into any lamp posts on the way to the store? I presume no one[3]. Our goal upon leaving the door is to buy some groceries and prepare them when getting home. Period. Of course we do not want to have accidents on the way. We want to return home safely. Also, we do not want to spend too much money. And we want to get home as quickly as possible because we want to see the latest episode of *Big Bang Theory*[4]. But we do not have goals of not running into lamp posts or of not getting run over by car. Neither do we specify goals for zero overspending or zero delays[5].

Doing the job safely (as swiftly and as cheaply as possible) is just a natural part of our process of doing groceries, not in the least because running into lamp posts interferes seriously with our main goal of doing some shopping and getting home safely.

Accepting that someone can get hurt is something completely different from planning to hurt someone and executing that plan. Just like not having a 'zero lamp post' goal does not mean that we set out to run into a couple of them on the way to the shop and back.

Another analogy: accepting that you can get wet when you get out in the rain (despite the fact that you brought a rain coat and an umbrella) is distinctly different from going out in the rain with the aim of getting wet. Again no 'Zero Wetness' policy needed. And, if you set out with the aim to get wet, why not make things easier for yourself and leave the umbrella and raincoat at home? Or take a shower.

If you do not need 'Zero goals' for activities like these, why would you need them in safety?[6] Why not rather find some more positive measure for safety instead of relying on super-reactive and random outcome indicators?

---

[1] Based on Myth 73 from *Safety Myth 101*.

[2] Just for the sake of clarification: I am not a native English speaker. I have understood that there are nuances between the words goal, target and objective, but frankly these escape me. And they probably also escape others because according to the online Merriam-Webster the meaning of target and goal are exactly the same, while Wikipedia identifies objective as a synonym for goal. So I presume that these nuances are probably meanings attached to them by people without looking at the commonly used definitions. I will therefore use them relatively interchangeably, although I will mainly try to stick to the word goal.

[3] If anyone does set this goal explicitly, please contact me. You must be an interesting person.

[4] Fill in your favourite TV show here. It is sad to see that at the time of writing these lines BBT has stopped and I have been unable to find a suitable replacement so far.

[5] By the way, just think of the downside of such a goal. It might prevent helping that old lady crossing the street or come in the way of valuable (but unmeasurable) social interactions with friends or neighbours that you coincidentally meet on the way. Or, more importantly (in case you are single), you may miss getting to know that nice girl/guy in the vegetable section that leads to a date and the love of your life…

[6] Feel free and try to convince me otherwise. Good arguments can be sent to the editorial address.

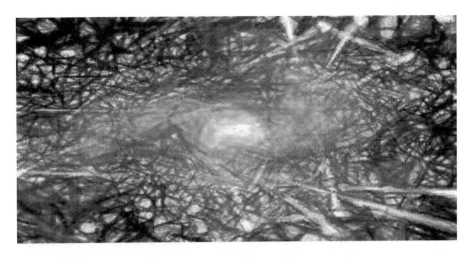

The More Data, the Better[1]

-Data- -Benchmarking- -Uncertainty-

Many organisations gather as much as possible under the trendy[2] moniker of Big Data and think that this will automatically improve their Safety Management (and other business areas). One of the funniest quotes in this regard comes from Dan Ariely:

> "Big data is like teenage sex: everyone talks about it, nobody really knows how to do it, everyone thinks everyone else is doing it, so everyone claims they are doing it"[3].

I am not entirely sure what Ariely meant to say by this, but I can pick some messages from this quote as my personal interpretation: 1) Not everyone who says that they are working with Big Data actually does this, or does it in an useful way. 2) Benchmarking, looking at what others do, may be meaningless because you may be looking at useless applications. 3) Like teenagers fumbling around, many organisations gather data without a plan or knowing what they need. 4) Many organisations do not have the skill (yet) to actually do something worthwhile with the data - what it means, what they can learn from it, and/or how to use them to affect goals.

Also Nate Silver cautions about Big Data[4]. There is promise, but also major pitfalls - the signal and noise from his book's title. One problem is that these days, thanks to automation, computers and the internet, the noise is increasing faster than the signal and may be more distracting than ever before. Even though people love to predict things, they are not very good at it. One thing to keep in mind is that we can never make perfectly objective predictions; we will always draw in some kind of subjective point of view. So we must think about our ideas and how to test them.

Gerd Gigerenzer agrees[5]. He says that we often cannot see the forest for the trees because of the overload of data. One must realise that there is a difference between data and information. The latter can be useful, the former is often distracting.

Gigerenzer talks about the desirability of perfect memory - it is not! We have to forget so that we can generalise and make things abstract. A memory entirely composed of details is unable to think on an abstract level. Too much detailed memory impairs the mind's ability to abstract, infer and learn. It is important to discard some data, or make it more abstract in order to get information - Silver's signal. A trend is often more important than many detailed single cases, although we have to be cautious there too, because humans have a knack for seeing patterns, also where no patterns are found and they are just looking at noise.

Another thing worth thinking about is if we are dealing with well-known areas or uncertainty. In situations of uncertainty less information may be more useful. It is easier to pick the signal from the noise and react on the important cues. Gigerenzer says that good decision making in a partly uncertain world requires ignoring part of the available information, and as a consequence, performing less complex estimations because of the robustness problem. People do not, like it is often assumed, rationally weigh the pros and cons of a situation based on all information relevant to the case, but rather make a decision with the limited information available - as process coined as satisficing by Herbert Simon[6]. Would humans indeed make decisions on all relevant data, we would not get anywhere. Instead we use that which we think is satisfactory and then make a decision often based on intuition, heuristics or gut instinct[7].

Sometimes, less really is more[8].

[1] Based on Myth 7 from *Safety Myth 101*.

[2] If you think that 'Big Data' is something new of 'our time', think again. It may be trendy, but 'Big Data' is really nothing new, no matter what consultants and the media may try to tell you. The only thing really new is our ever-increasing capacity to crunch and manipulate it. Check for example the following paper that takes a look at historic use of 'Big Data' within safety:

Swuste, P.H.J.J. (2016) Is Big Data Risk Assessment a Novelty? *Safety and Reliability*, 36 (3): 134-152. doi: 10.1080/09617353.2016.1252084.

[3] Dan Ariely posted it on his Facebook page in 2013:

https://www.facebook.com/dan.ariely/posts/904383595868 (checked 21 July 2019)

[4] Silver, N.R. (2012) *The Signal And The Noise*. London: Penguin.

[5] Gigerenzer, G. (2010) *Rationality For Mortals - How People Cope With Uncertainty*. Oxford: Oxford University Press.

[6] Simon, H.A. (1969) *The Sciences of the Artificial*. Cambridge, MA: MIT Press.

[7] Good reading here:

Klein, G.A. (1999) *Sources of Power: How People make Decisions*. Cambridge: MIT Press.

Gigerenzer, G. (2007) *Gut Feelings - Short Cuts To Better Decision Making*. London: Penguin.

Gladwell, M. (2005) *Blink: The Power of Thinking Without Thinking*. Columbus: Back Bay Books/Little, Brown and Company.

Also Gigerenzer's other books like *Rationality for Mortals* or *Risk Savvy* discuss the subject.

[8] A different subject entirely, but as Barry Schwartz argues also more choice is not always better. He has a TED Talk about the 'Paradox of Choice': some choice is better than no choice, but more choice is not always better than some choice (https://www.ted.com/talks/barry_schwartz_on_the_paradox_of_choice). I have yet to read his book *The Paradox of Choice - Why More Is Less*, but judging from his other work I presume it is interesting.

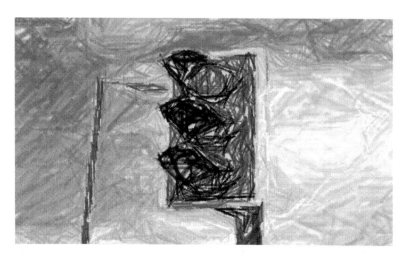

Red = Bad[1]

-Red- -Indicators- -Action-

Managers are often busy people that have little time or patience for detail and thick reports. So often they are quick to ask for a summary. When it comes to safety metrics, this often boils down to aggregating everything into one or few index numbers or in simplifying a lot of data into colours or smiley faces instead of numbers and a lot of text[2].

This has clear advantages, not in the least with regard to efficiency, since it prevents discussions about details, like if a number should be 23 or 24 where this is irrelevant for the big picture. Often more time is spent on discussing what shall be included or excluded from the statistics than is spent on finding out what the problem really is, what can be learned, and deciding on effective actions.

But beware, smileys and colours also include a possible drawback, namely that they simplify rich information and thereby over communicate part of the message, drown out nuance and context and in effect hide much of the information. They may also lead to a mechanistic process of decision making where more richness and discussion is needed. And, of course, there is often the risk that traffic lights and numerical goals may become an end in itself which leads to unwanted effects, like when responsible managers manage quantity, not quality.

Another problem is the intuitive reaction that people have regarding colours. Green usually signals growth and safety. Red, on the other hand, is a colour that we automatically relate to danger and warnings. A red traffic light means STOP. Red numbers on your bank account are definitely not good. When you are in the red area of a risk matrix, we are talking about high or even unacceptable risk. In nature red is also often a warning signal like poisonous berries or bugs[3].

Through the way we intuitively understand colours, we unconsciously attach meaning to them without often even checking if this is correct. Often it is automatically assumed that a red indicator means that things look bad and that the red indicator needs to be eliminated as soon as possible and at all costs[4]. But, 'jumping on red' can mean starting sub-optimal and unnecessary actions that use up resources that would be better spent elsewhere[5].

This reminds me of an episode at a previous employer. As part of 'improving the safety culture'[6], it was decided to improve the follow up of actions after incidents, near misses, inspections and audits. So top management adopted a 'Zero Overdue Actions' policy and made it part of the weekly management team meeting. As a consequence, all underlying units started to make sure that they had no overdue deadlines. After a few weeks, it became clear that one way of reaching this goal was to enter the tracking system during the weekend and move all the deadlines in the 'danger zone' a few weeks forward. In the Monday management meeting, things then looked quite 'rosey'.

The intention of the 'Zero Overdue Actions' policy was undoubtedly positive, but it quickly turned out that because the metric was perceived as so important, people found ways to look better than they were doing, or were able to do. As a negative side effect, they started using time on administratively reaching their goal, instead of using these resources for actual improvement (which was the original objective, of course). At some point, one manager realised this and decided to not move any deadlines anymore and burn precious resources on 'looking good'. Her intent was to either set more realistic deadlines, or make an underlying problem (namely lack of resources to complete all the actions) visible to top management. This clearly required some 'balls', but in the end it led to better safety management, and a more relaxed attitude to 'Zero'.

Instead of seeing the red indicator as a flag that indicates that this situation is unacceptable we should first look at the context and the things that lie behind the indicator. Only after thorough study action may be necessary - and then in balance with other objectives. And as illustrated, 'red' can help making other issues visible.

In conclusion: we need a more careful response to 'red'. Or we maybe even need a radically different attitude towards 'red', namely one of embracing the 'bad' news and using 'red' as an indicator for possible improvement. And the opposite is probably even truer. One should be suspicious of whether the 'green' is really as good as it looks. When presented with a report that has only positive information, make sure to ask:

"Where is the bad news"?

###

[1] Based on Myth 79 from *Safety Myth 101*.

[2] This was also one of the factors that was mentioned during the Columbia space shuttle investigation. A lot of relevant information was presented to management in crisp and nested bullet points and a lot of information was lost in translation. Check for example:

https://nobullets.wordpress.com/2008/01/17/the-disasterous-consequence-of-bullet-points-a-real-life-example/ (checked 21 July 2019)

[3] But, confusingly also meant to attract positive attention like red flowers or red lipstick…

[4] I am no neuroscientist, but it sounds almost as if this is a primal reaction from our amygdala. We see an immediate hazard and have the irresistible urge to react on it right away (which also applies to the red lipstick, by the way).

[5] Check what is said about interventionism elsewhere in this book.

[6] I would rather not step into the wasp's nest that this seemingly simple statement conceals…

Forget SMART. Go Fuzzy

-SMART- -Goals- -Side effects-

It is common management (or consultant) wisdom that objectives are supposed to be SMART: Specific, Measurable, Acceptable, Realistic, and Timebound. This credo is repeated a number of times in this book, notably to point out some weaknesses of 'Zero' goals.

However, like anything, SMART also comes with some disadvantages, dark sides even. This reminded me of a Dutch blog[1] that a friend forwarded to me about 15 years ago. The author, Peter Markensteijn, claimed: *Stop SMART, be FUZZY!* Some interesting reflections here.

One main problem, according to Markensteijn, is turning a 'smart' *guideline* as SMART into a *dogma*. Dogmatic approaches are almost always problematic and we should realise that not everything that we try to achieve or set out to do needs to be SMART. In fact, many things even suffer of a SMART-treatment. Love is not SMART. Family life tends mostly to be not SMART (some elements, like the kids' bed times are very SMART, however). Also, I am sure that much of your entertainment and leisure is as SMART-less as possible[2].

When SMART becomes your dogma, you may consider anything that is not SMART as less important. This provides you a blanket reason to reject things for not being SMART. You may then engage in strained attempts to force objectives into a SMART-straightjacket. Or the opposite happens: your ambitions and goals become bloodless and not inspiring, but safe, because SMART also means accountable…

When you treat the elements of S.M.A.R.T. too rigidly or too dogmatic several negative side effects may rear their ugly heads. Take for example 'Specific'. If this term is taken too literally, it means that you need to spell out in great detail what you set out to achieve and often also how. And how do you do that? Say you want to improve something, but it is a bit unclear exactly what the final result will be. That is unacceptable from the SMART-perspective, and 'better' is not specific enough! But even if you describe beforehand very specifically the final result, how does that deal with uncertainties, randomness and surprises? Also, exploring and learning are not necessarily specific. However, these are important goals that we need to do, even though they are not SMART.

The 'M' is often connected to the first letter, especially when seeing 'Measurable' as purely quantitative. When you express something in a number, it becomes both specific and measurable. However, a known saying tells us that not everything that counts is countable and I listed a couple of examples above. Also, as you have seen throughout this book, numbers tend to turn into goals very quickly and then the creative creatures that humans are discover ways to easily manipulate the numbers instead of doing the hard work.

The next two letters, 'Acceptable' and 'Realistic' used to be my favourites, because they could be used to suggest involvement and communication (we agree on a goal and then accept it) and acknowledge limitations (for example by scaling the ambitions in accordance to available resources). At the same time, these two can have a 'damping' effect on ambitions (as learning, exploring, improving) because we go as far as the SMART goal and no further. Or, as suggested, that we go for goals that we are certain to reach. SMART then leads to defensive practices.

The final letter, 'T', is often problematic in several ways. Not always are we able to attach some kind of timeframe to a goal, for example because of the many uncertainties underway. From the onset, often deadlines are too optimistic. We almost always underestimate the time we really need, or ignore the random disturbances that will rear their heads. Optimistic (unrealistic) deadlines can also be imposed because of political reasons, or because it has been promised to the public, clients or someone higher up in the system by others (so much for acceptable...).

Neither should the deadline be used too rigidly for SMART accountability, because there are often very legitimate reasons to deviate, as for example conflicting objectives, and unforeseen events. If this is the case, it may be wise to go for super safe deadlines. Or just hope that they are forgotten altogether.

Accountability according to SMART-objectives leads to:

- Goals that are safe and not ambitious.
- Demotivating effects, either because the accountability is felt as unfair, the goal is unachievable, or the goals are boring, bloodless and mechanic.
- Attempts to make things SEP - Somebody Else's Problem.

Do not get me wrong - applying SMART as a guideline does have its advantages, but as any tool it needs to be handled with skill and deliberation. John Maynard Keynes dictum that it is better to be roughly right than precisely wrong suggests that also SMART has some grey zones. Apply some Fuzziness to your approach!

###

[1] http://www.markensteijn.com/smart.htm (checked 20 July 2019)

[2] Even though I do acknowledge that some people's work-out regimes, obsession with 'To Do' lists and fanatic zeal to have a good time and demonstrate this to the world through Facebook and Instagram clearly contradicts my statement…

Intervention, NOW![1]

-Statistics- -Action- -Patterns-

One thing that I often come across and that annoys me endlessly is the waste of resources and effort on non-existing problems at the cost of more important things. This happens especially after (serious) accidents or if the statistics do something 'strange' that is interpreted by many people as a signal that something *must* be done. Often this is a symptom of people being unable to handle or understand disorder and randomness - or that they are lured into action (intentionally or not) as can be seen in the example in the *Lies, Damn Lies...* chapter.

It may also be a consequence of agency problems - people initiate actions because they profit from them. This is often seen in highly political environments (where I have been working for most of the last decade). But also in more common industry. There you may find managers, union members, consultants and even Safety Professionals who have their own agenda for pushing forward an unnecessary action.

This kind of interventionism makes things fragile[2] because it leads us to work on the wrong things. Additionally, it often creates negative side effects because things get more complex and because of that, there may be unforeseen interactions, especially if actions are done in a rushed way to demonstrate leadership or decisiveness.

Jop Groeneweg has a great example in his book *Controlling The Controllable*[3] that can serve very well for explaining the point. Let us imagine a situation where an accident occurs on average every tenth week. This can be a factory, a chemical plant, a major construction project, or a busy intersection in a large town. An average year may look like this (with the number of accidents on the y-axis and the week number on the x-axis):

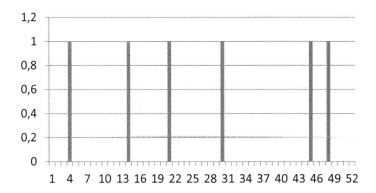

Things have been roughly like this for several years. Then, all of a sudden something odd happens - we get three accidents in three successive weeks:

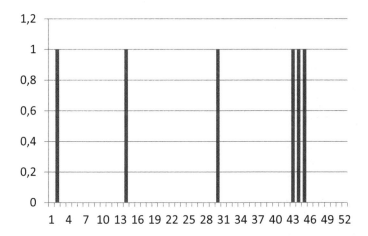

It is very likely that in week 45 someone will start to raise the alarm because accidents are not supposed to happen that frequently. Some will claim that the safety situation deteriorates and a safety campaign or some other action is needed. Now! But most likely, there is nothing really out of the ordinary here[4]. It is only the perception and wrong understanding of a cluster of incidents happening close to each other. As mentioned earlier in the chapter on correlation, we think that we see a pattern and we assign meaning to it, and we urge to react to it.

However, unless there is a causal link we should resist that urge. The cluster or perceived pattern should be investigated to find out if there is anything there. But do not rush an action out of the blue as often happens to "absolutely guarantee that something like this never can happen again". In our zeal to make sure that clusters (or certain types of 'bigger' events) never happen again, we overreact too quickly, overlook the real problems and come too quickly with over-tight control and an overkill of new rules.

A very typical example of this phenomenon was the public and political reaction to increased reports in the media of uncontrolled weapon discharges by the Norwegian police. The Norwegian police force is traditionally unarmed and trained to handle problems in the first place with alternative methods. Due to an increased threat level where military and police personnel might be the target of acts of terrorism, it was decided in the autumn of 2014 that uniformed police officers were to bear arms permanently (for a given period).

Uncontrolled discharges of firearms have the potential of doing serious harm, there is no question about this. But that they occur should not be a surprise, people make mistakes after all, even extremely well-trained professionals as police officers generally are. Neither should an increase in the number of uncontrolled discharges be a surprise. Experiences from abroad had shown that general armament led to an increased number of uncontrolled discharges. Everybody who has done some kind of activity (like typing letters into a computer as I am doing now), will have noticed that the more often one performs this activity, the more frequently one will make mistakes[5]. This was exactly what happened, but still the media jumped upon it. 'Concerned' politicians engaged themselves, no doubt rooted in misunderstanding of the significance of unwanted events[6] along with using the situation to further their own political agendas. For a while sub-optimal actions were a consequence of the increasing political pressure[7]. Until things went back to normal for police officers in early 2016.

Clusters are often perfectly explainable from the context (environment, time of the year, changes in registration) or plain randomness. And things like these are often perfectly able to take care of themselves because of safety programs that are in place. These programs will more often than not be affected in a negative way if yet another action is added; through interference, or because resources will be redirected[8].

The sad thing is, of course, that when some action is performed that does not help or makes things worse, then often the situation will have taken care of itself (e.g. as a consequence of regression to the mean), but to the action-takers it will seem as if their action has had the desired effect. The negative side effects will only show after a long period and it will be hard to find its origin in this panic action.

Understanding this, making judgements like this, and actually deciding on not doing anything[9] and letting some occasions of disorder 'take care of themselves' requires competence. In High Reliability Organisation literature this is called "sensitivity for operation"[10].

---

[1] Originally based on parts of the *Agile Not Fragile* presentation with Nick Gardener at the EHSQ Elite Symposium in Amsterdam, November 2014 and published in a slightly different form as Myth 76 in *Safety Myth 101*.

[2] One of the arguments made by Nassim Taleb in his great book *Antifragile*: unnecessary intervention in a system will make it unstable and actually facilitate its failure.

Taleb, N.N. (2012) *Antifragile: Things that Gain from Disorder.* New York: Random House.

[3] Groeneweg, J. (1992) *Controlling the Controllable: The Management of Safety.* Leiden: DSWO Press.

[4] The yearly average is exactly the same and if you would plot in rolling averages they will be almost flat.

[5] In absolute numbers, of course. Relatively it is likely that you get better as experience increased. Until routine may cause you to become sloppy or overconfident again. An interesting subject that we are not going to discuss here and now.

[6] Professor Tor-Geir Myrher of the Norwegian Police Academy wrote a fine nuanced piece on the subject that illustrates that the risk of driving around in a car is much larger than these few uncontrolled discharges: http://www.nrk.no/ytring/bomskudd-om-politiskudd-1.12583303 (checked 22 July 2019)

[7] Scott A. Snook says in *Friendly Fire* that "Left unchecked, such organizational knee jerks provide the system with the necessary energy to kick off subsequent cycles of disaster". Snook's book deals with the shooting down of two US helicopters by US jet fighters which is somewhat comparable to unwanted weapon discharges. Snook interestingly mentions a congressional study commissioned to investigate the high rates of friendly fire during the Gulf war: actions to eliminate friendly fire will probably lead to a worse situation due to reduced combat effectiveness and thereby higher damage caused by the enemy.

Snook, S.A. (2000) *Friendly Fire.* Princeton: Princeton University Press.

[8] If you want to dive deeper into this, check the work of quality pioneers Walter A. Shewhart and W. Edwards Deming and their notions of common cause (or chance cause) and special cause (assignable cause). The latter comes as a surprise to you, while the former is variation that is 'naturally' present in your system and can be predicted. The use of control charts is helpful to determine whether one should act, or not.

[9] What we in Norway call to have 'is i magen', meaning: 'ice in the stomach'.

[10] Weick, K.E. & Sutcliffe, K.M. (2001) *Managing the Unexpected: Assuring High Performance in an Age of Complexity.* San Francisco: Jossey-Bass.

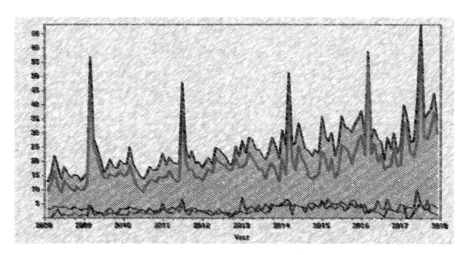

Ups and Downs: What Accident Statistics can tell us[1]

-Statistics- -Accidents- -Surrogates-

I do not read all the news about safety, but internet and social media often alert me to the main headlines. Like press releases that the Dutch Health and Safety Authority (Inspectie SZW) is concerned about the number of accidents that apparently has been on the rise for the past few years - while they at the same time tell us that the likelihood of having an occupational accident in the Netherlands is very low[2]. Other organisations come with similar messages. Maybe it is a good moment to reflect on what these metrics and news items can tell us.

Do mind, I do not have any concrete answers. I do have many questions, however, and thinking about those may help us to deal with statistics in a healthy way.

Primal reaction

Let us start by wondering how this affects us. Accidents are horrible, in particular when people lose their lives or are permanently injured, either physically or mentally. Events like that demand our attention and appeal to our emotions. Those primal reactions quickly lead to social, political and moral pressure to do 'something'. Suddenly there is this *sense of urgency*: this horrible thing shall never happen again!

But... is that primary reaction always the best? Often, the reaction on accidents and statistics is little but a knee-jerk. Unthinkingly one jumps to the first 'cause' at hand ("human error", "bad safety culture") and comes up with a quick fix ("more regulatory oversight", "stricter rules", "a campaign"). Often, these are ineffective and draw resources away from other, structural safety initiatives. The smart thing to do would therefore be to think things over, before acting.

A Measure for Safety?

Accidents are horrible, but what do they actually tell us about safety? Instinctively we think that "many accidents = unsafe". The number of accidents surely gives some kind of indication about (un)safety, but this is rather limited. And this works both ways.

We perform countless 'unsafe acts' without them ever resulting in an accident. Say, someone gets into his car after an evening of heavy boozing, and arrives home safely without so much as a scratch. No one will think of calling that scenario particularly safe, the term to describe it would rather be 'lucky'. No accident is not necessarily safe.

What about the opposite? Does an accident mean that the situation or act was unsafe? Intuitively we may be inclined to answer, "Of course, else there had not been an accident". But that is speaking with hindsight. Before the accident happened, one probably assumed that things were safe. That assumption may have been correct, and maybe false.

The accident may be the result of an unforeseen combination of circumstances, but also of an accepted risk. After all, we take many risks willingly. If you build your house in a flood plain, you should not be surprised if you get wet feet every once in a while. We often regard a one-in-a-million chance as safe, but that does not mean that no accident can happen. Then there are the risks we cannot fully control, despite our best efforts. Which is the prime reason why airbags, seatbelts and energy absorption zones exist.

Accidents are an even worse measure for safety when it comes to injuries. Randomness plays an even larger role. One and the same accident, for example a collision of a car on a railway level crossing, can have limited consequences (the driver is physically unharmed), serious consequences (the only person in the car, the driver, is killed) or extremely serious (a family of five dies in the accident). The accident was the same; the consequences are very diverse.

Sign for urgent action?

What does a peak or an increasing or declining line actually tell us? Our brains are wired to recognize patterns. This ability helps us to function effectively and efficiently. Sometimes we perceive patterns that are not there, however, and we attribute these perceived patterns some significance that they do not have. Three accidents on three successive days does not necessarily mean that suddenly a wave of unsafety has struck us.

If you see a peak, or some decrease of increase, put it into context. Check whether where this happens (e.g. circumstances, sector, or location) really is the 'main' problem, or if there are maybe matters that deserve more attention. For example, more people die as the consequence of exposure to various chemicals than from occupational accidents.

Numbers can vary heavily over the years. Do look into the reasons for these fluctuations. Sometimes this can be randomness. Sometimes you can find a factor that correlates. If activity in the construction business doubles, it should be not surprising that the number of accidents goes up.

Interests?

Look always how the numbers are presented. Lying, or telling half-truths, with help of statistics is rather easy. Statistics are easy to manipulate without even faking the numbers. You can amplify your message by adjusting scales, cutting them, by limiting to a certain period, by extending the period, by presenting things in percentages, ratios or in absolute numbers.

Three fatalities per year on level crossings sounds serious; 0,006 fatalities per level crossing with barriers is considerably less serious and 0,0009 fatalities per level crossing will not worry many people. Or you can make an increase in the number of fatalities look dramatic by only looking at the previous year, and ignoring the period that came before (Cobouw did this in the Netherlands, declaring 2016 a "disaster year" while looking at a five year period did not show any pattern[3]).

Ask yourself what message the way of presenting is meant to support and how the numbers would look (and what they would say) if they were presented in another way. When dramatic numbers are presented it is always wise to stop for a moment and wonder what interests this message serves. This message is not always to the benefit of safety!

A better approach

Do not regard a number, a trend or a peak as some kind of an answer; something that leads to apparently 'decisive' panic actions. Rather regard them as something that tickles your curiosity. Something that sparks the question "Hey, I wonder why this is how it is". Something to be regarded in an historical perspective and its context.

Accident metrics? My advice: do not give them more attention than they deserve from a professional safety perspective. Accidents send us a signal that we most likely have one or more opportunities for improvement. They give information about unknown or unrecognized risks. About unexpected side effects and competing objectives. Approach that with sober and critical thinking, and not with a knee-jerk.

###

---

[1] This chapter is loosely based on an article I wrote in preparation of the Congres Veilig Werken on 11 April 2018 in Ahoy, Rotterdam. You can find the original (in Dutch) here: http://arbo-online.nl/ongevallencijfers-het-is-maar-hoe-je-ernaar-kijkt/ (checked 15 July 2019)

[2] https://www.inspectieszw.nl/actueel/nieuws/2017/12/13/gezond-veilig-en-eerlijk-werk-voor-iedereen (checked 15 July 2019)

[3] http://arbo-online.nl/2016-rampjaar-voor-veiligheid-in-bouw/ (checked 15 July 2019)

$$p(x) = -G(-x^2)/[xH(-x^2)].$$
$$\pi k \leq p0 - \alpha_0 \leq \pi/2 + 2\pi k, \quad p = 2\mathcal{V}_0 + (1/2)[\text{sg } A_1 - \text{sg } (A$$
$$= \sum_{j=0, j \neq p} A_j \rho^j \cos\left[(p-j)\theta - \alpha_j\right] + \rho^p. \quad \Delta_L \arg f(z) = (\pi/2)(S_1 +$$
$$\tilde{G}(u) = \prod_{k=1}^{\mu}(u + u_k)G_0(u), \quad \Re[\rho^r f(z)/u_p.] - \sum$$
$$(A_{n-1}A_n)] \quad p(x) = -G(-x^2)/[xH(-x^2)].$$
$$p = 2\mathcal{V}_0 \quad \rho^p > \sum_{j=0, j \neq p}^{n} A_j \rho^j, \quad -\pi/2 + 2\pi k \leq p0 - \alpha_0$$

Causal Confusion[1]

-Science- -Causation- -Behaviour-

If you set out to find Safety Myths and Misunderstandings, incidents and causes are a rich field, especially when someone tries to apply measurements to them. Here is another illustration.

There was this survey, intended to test some hypotheses about the human factor in safety and collect data for a 'scientific' article about these hypotheses. Information was gathered through an online survey tool that questioned safety professionals about the most recent incidents they were involved in as investigators.

Participants were asked to what degree four factors ('causes') had contributed to the incident. Participants had to assign a score between 0 and 100% to each factor, with a total of 100% for the four factors.

......% Technical

......% System

......% Culture

......% Behaviour

At this point I stopped reading and decided not to participate and wondered if I should ask the person behind the survey (of whom I had a rather high opinion before, and so I did engage in a discussion - results pending) to stop this nonsense because this is so wrong on so many levels. Here are a few issues that I have with this 'research':

- Obviously, this is an oversimplification. Why these four factors? What model are these four factors based on? What about other factors, for example external factors, like forces of nature?

- What level of analysis of the incidents are we talking about anyway? Behaviour is usually very downstream (close to the incident) while culture and system tend to be more upstream (greater distance to incident).
- How do you ensure that this is going to be a (somewhat) representative research? How do you ensure correct scope and applicability of the findings? How do you ensure that the incidents in the survey are (somewhat) representative? Is it okay to include complex cases and more trivial OHS incidents in the same survey? And, how would you know? The only indication one can get is from the first questions that differentiate between near misses and accidents, and ask for the outcome of the incident. But, mind you: outcome says nothing (!!) about the case's complexity.
- How are you going to ensure interrater reliability such that each participant answers more or less from the same frame of mind and definitions? Besides, the definition of some terms (especially culture) was rather questionable.
- What is the quality of the investigations this survey is based on? Typically many investigations stop when they come across a convenient cause (often behaviour) and do not look further.
- What is the competence of the people who are going to answer? The survey was open on the World Wide Web, so anyone could participate.
- How are participants supposed to judge the contribution of a causal factor? And how would you know their method? Will they be counting how often a factor is mentioned (which is useless and arbitrary)? Will they do this by assigning a measure of importance? If so, does that mean that something on a higher organisational level should have more weight? Or should it be the reverse? Should something closer to the accident have more weight? What about underlying factors that affect more than one other factor? And so on.

This only scratches the surface of my concerns. Online newspaper, do opinion polls on this level, and the quality that comes out of this survey will probably not be any better than that. So please, stop calling it scientific research.

Before even the first word of the report is written, I suspect that the results are going to be an arbitrary opinion poll at best. Most likely, however, they are going to be extremely questionable. It might have been better to take a generally 'accepted' number with a more or less known bias (like Heinrich's infamous 88%), than come with a shaky survey that will only lead to even more confusion - even if it would 'find' the opposite of what Heinrich wrote many decades ago.

It *is* important to look into the role of human factors in safety and incidents. But please let us do it properly and not by means of some make-believe-research. *The First Law of Quality Assurance* does apply for full: Shit in = Shit out. Things like this will do harm to safety, firstly because of the confusion it may create. Secondly because it looks like safety people cannot get basic science right.

Having said that… Of course, there is also a different possibility. The mentioned survey is not about incident investigation at all, but about the biases and gullibility of safety professionals… I hope the latter (and still then some of my concerns apply), but fear the other alternative.

---

[1] Based on a blog from June 2016 that was written rather spontaneously. I am afraid that peers writing or saying 'stupid' stuff is a never ending inspiration, especially when there is this feeling that this is done by someone who really should know better (yeah, I can be awfully normative and judgemental - sorry). In this case, I also tried to argue per mail, but the author would not or could not listen or be convinced. Even worse, he actually included the results in his next book, but without explaining where they came from.

Zero, Zero, Nothing: A Vision with Zero Need of Zero-Goals[1]

-Zero- -Goals- -SMART-

"Zero accidents" has a major attraction. It intuitively appeals to us; after all, we do not want anyone being hurt or killed at work, or because of our activities. Recently, there was this online discussion that started with the sincere question "How safe is safe enough?" The very first reaction - applauded from various sides - was "Zero" accompanied by a tale about the enormous reduction in lost time incidents that a particular company had achieved thanks to a safety campaign. And so on. You know the stories. However, 'zero' comes packed with problems.

Does Zero mean safe?

Firstly, we have to ask ourselves whether 'zero accidents' really is a measure of safety. More fundamentally, what does the number of accidents actually tell us about safety? Say I decide to blow-dry my hair while taking a bath. When I manage to get out of the tub without being electrocuted, that means that I have realised 'zero', but was this operation safe? The classic example is obviously Deepwater Horizon with seven years without a lost-time accident before the installation went up in flames and smoke.

Absence of accidents is not the same as the presence of safety. Outcome indicators like the number of fatalities, injuries or accidents are at best weak indicators and goals for safety. We can read little out of this kind of metrics. Maybe 'zero' means that the work happened safely, maybe they were just lucky (like yours truly in the tub), maybe they did not measure properly, or incomplete with regard to the risks (like on the Deep Water Horizon) or maybe there is just massive underreporting.

The foundation

The foundations of 'zero' are weak. It builds upon the unrealistic premises that all accidents are preventable. That is only possible in a utopic, ideal world where everything can be controlled, things are perfectly predictable and there are no surprises. Man, machine and systems work like a Swiss clock (even better than that) and external influences are completely absent, just like variables such as human mood swings, distraction, conflicting objectives, and shortage of resources, time and the like[2].

Obviously, that is an unrealistic scenario. People and organisations *do* have limited knowledge and resources; all the while, they have to handle a number of challenges simultaneously. Given these limitations one has to make choices, as well as possible under the circumstances. We just cannot prevent everything. Even more important, we *do not want to* prevent absolutely everything. Some things we can live with perfectly fine, or we must learn to live with them. That is a clear reason for having a 'reasonably' criterion. In management language: a 'zero goal' is not SMART[3]!

Zero what?

Besides, in what area are you aiming for 'zero'? Fatalities? Injuries? A noble aspiration surely, but one problem is that consequences in many scenarios are rather random. Hard to predict and hard to steer. Except if you aim for risk reduction to 'zero', which is simply impossible.

Some organisations go as far as claiming to strive for "zero incidents" or "zero errors". That is definitely an unlucky approach. Learning of 'failure', 'errors' or 'events' is an important way to work towards improvement. If you are steering towards a low metric for these things, however, this might lead to zero reports which might dry up your most important source of information.

Another problem with zero-accident-goals is that they often only deal with 'hard' safety. The biggest problem for employees, however, may not be in the realms of safety, but rather be related to occupational health. Exposure to harmful chemicals, biologic substances, and physical or psychological stress are a much greater problem when we look at long-term effects, lost time and fatalities[4].

Finishing line?

Some organisations manage to reach 'zero' - at least during a certain period. The question then arises: "Now what?" One problem is that when you make it to 'zero', this could give people a wrong impression and lull them into sleep. It suggests that the situation is safe as long no accidents happen. That might not be the case at all. Maybe there have been no accidents by sheer luck, or because other circumstances compensated all that time.

Even if we regard 'zero' as a commitment to continuous improvement, what direction should you go after you have reached 'zero'? Basically, there is only one way to go, and that is back. Is that what you want? Of course not! To hold a certain level at all cost can be extremely frustrating, however, and not exactly motivating. Besides, people will be afraid to spoil the seemingly perfect performance.

You can also wonder how balanced is a zero vision really. Organisations must always take other objectives and interests into account, because believe it or not, not one organisation exists with the prime goal of being safe.

Side effects

As the history of humanity has taught us, ambitious goals contribute to reaching exceptional performances. Numerical objectives can be a useful tool to get people and organisations in motion and keep the forward movement. At the same time, it can be highly frustrating if you raise the bar to unrealistic levels, especially when we are talking about absolute measures like 'zero'.

Only a minor disturbance is needed to fail. The 'score' is the ruined for the remainder of that period. This does not really motivate and can lead to 'creative' use of definitions and categories, and that 'bad' news is censored out. Just think of the Volkswagen emission scandal.

René Amalberti has researched the added value of striving for even more safety within ultra-safe systems and reached a couple of interesting conclusions. For example, that unrealistic expectations with regard to safety very well might end to speeding up the end of an ultra-safe system[5].

Ethics!

An often heard argument is that 'zero' can be the only ethically and morally acceptable goal, because you just cannot have an objective that allows harm or even death. That is complete nonsense for a number of reasons. For example, because this totally disregards the principle of 'reasonable', the need to balance diverse and conflicting objectives and life itself: if you get out of your bed in the morning to participate in what we call living (and besides, also if you decide to stay in bed) you accept implicitly that you may encounter some harm. This may be highly unlikely, but still.

Those who feel that 'zero accidents' is the only morally acceptable 'goal', should realise that we do not need goals for accidents at all. Let us rather find other, better, preferably positive, performance indicators. And let us monitor incidents and accidents purely for the sake of mandatory statistics, use them as opportunities for learning and maybe follow them as an indicator, but not as a goal.

Speaking about ethics, how morally acceptable is it really to require perfection (= 'zero') from fallible humans, machines and systems? Perfectionism has positive sides, because it can motivate individuals to strive for ambitious goals. On the other hand, it can also be a destructive factor, and it is even a psychological disorder. Not exactly something to strive for[6].

In connection to the Vision Zero movement, I have seen statements that accidents do not belong to the identity of the organisation[7]. That kind of nonsense annoys me a lot. Although there definitely is a number of mistakes in my life that I rather not would have committed, these experiences have contributed to getting me where I am today. The very same applies also to organisations and accidents. Aviation, railways or automobiles would not have today's level of safety if it were not for the accidents that gave us an opportunity to learn. No matter how sad the consequences have been, these accidents have absolutely been an essential part of the identity, and I think it is hugely disrespectful of the victims to deny this!

So, is 'zero' completely useless?

Let us be clear: I am not against the striving for no accidents or even against a zero vision. This, however, must never turn into a target. There is a world of difference between a target (that is supposed to be concrete and SMART) and a vision (*"I have a dream"*).

A vision is a dream about where we want to be. It is about striving for improvement on the (very) long term. Like reaching for the stars, it is something of which we must realise that we will most likely never reach it. However, striving for it could be worthwhile nevertheless. The right approach is then to "combine an ambitious, inspiring long term vision with quantified interim targets"[8], instead of running unthinkingly behind some nice sounding slogan.

A vision has most of all a symbolic value: it can be used to communicate commitment for continuous improvement. This must be balanced with realism, however. A major problem is that many do not get the symbolism and take the 'zero' too literal. That turns 'zero' immediately into some kind of target, with all kinds of unwanted side effects, including not reporting incidents, creative accounting (e.g. by stretching definitions) or the emergence of a culture in which people blame each other for ruining a perfect score.

Often "zero vision" and ambitious targets are said to play an important role in realising safety improvements[9]. We should ask ourselves, however, if we are rather talking about correlation instead of a causal connection. An organisation that gives her utmost, will most likely also have a vision. Embracing just a "zero vision" because many other organisations do the same will not lead to improvement in itself, for that you will first need a solid safety program.

And so?

Again, you do not need 'zero' as a target. As we saw, the number of accidents or injuries is a weak measure of safety. Striving for improvement and caring for our people should be sufficient. We cannot prevent everything, but that does not diminish the responsibility to do our utter best - within reasonable limits.

James Reason puts it very well:

> "Safety is a guerrilla war that you will probably lose (since entropy gets us all in the end), but you can still do the best you can."[10]

Let us take these wise words at hard, and get working. We cannot prevent all accidents and reach 'zero' in a sustainable way. At least we can prevent a great many accidents by working systematically and structurally. Hopefully, we will manage to prevent the ones that matter the most. Good luck!

###

[1] This is a reworked translation of the article that I wrote for the February 2018 edition of NVVK Info, which had 'Zero' as the main subject.

Busch, C. (2018) Nul, Nul, Niks. Een Visie met Nul Behoefte aan Nul-Doelstellingen. *NVVK Info*, 27 (1): 18-20.

Find the original article at https://de.calameo.com/read/0027057436e6e80c8b612.

[2] Busch, C. (2016) *Safety Myth 101*. Mysen: Mind The Risk.

[3] In case you forgot, SMART means: Specific, Measurable, Acceptable, Realistic, and Timebound.

[4] Townsend, A.S. (2014) *Safety Can't Be Measured: An Evidence-based Approach to Improving Risk Reduction*. Farnham: Gower Publishing.

[5] Amalberti, R. (2001) The Paradoxes of Almost Totally Safe Transportation Systems. *Safety Science*, 37 (2): 109-126.

[6] Long, R. (2012) *For the Love of Zero: Human Fallibility and Risk*. Kambah, ACT: Scotoma Press.

[7] Zwetsloot, G.I.J.M. (2016) De Nul Ongevallen Visie: een Nieuw Perspectief voor het Verbeteren van Veiligheid. *Tijdschrift voor Toegepaste Arbowetenschap*, 29 (2): 61-64.

[8] Groot-Mesken, J. de (2014) *De Waarde van Nul. Nulvisies en Verkeersveiligheidsbeleid. (R-2014-8)*. Den Haag: Stichting Wetenschappelijk Onderzoek Verkeersveiligheid.

[9] Zwetsloot, G.I.J.M. et.al. (2017) The Importance of Commitment, Communication, Culture and Learning for the Implementation of the Zero Accident Vision in 27 Companies in Europe. *Safety Science*, 96: 22-32.

[10] Reason, J. (2008) *The Human Contribution*. Farnham: Ashgate.

You Can Manage What You Measure - But Does It Help?[1]

During our vacations, we tend to have some nice walks in the Swedish woods. A while ago, I bought my wife an iPod with an included step counter (and all kind of other fancy 'health' functions and statistics). She took this device when we went for a walk, just for fun to see how far it would be around the lake and such.

At one point, my wife mentioned that she recently had seen a news item[2] as well as a scientific article that mentioned research[3] which had 'shown' that step counters and similar devices did not work if you wanted to lose weight. The article tells us that "Devices that monitor and provide feedback on physical activity may not offer an advantage over standard behavioural weight loss approaches".

That is interesting, because it sounds really counter-intuitive at first. Besides, has other research not 'found' the opposite? But then, this is a rather typical phenomenon. Often you can find research[4] and sources[5] that show different results. All the more reason to look critically at the sources and methods to find out what the research or source really is worth.

But that was not what I wanted to discuss at this point. Let us assume that the recent research is right and that these activity-tracking devices indeed do not help as we assume they would do. What the article does not mention is why that would be so. Here is my hypothesis:

I am fairly sure that we are dealing with a typical example of the means becoming the goal. Someone has at some point come with some advisable number of steps that one should go a day in order to stay healthy or lose weight. 10.000 is a typical number -

what a coincidence that it would be such a nice round one (one would expect something more differentiated - also TNO makes some critical remarks). But whatever…

Assuming that it is 10.000, what happens is that many people replace their original goal (getting healthier, losing some weight, getting in better shape) with reaching the numerical goal (go 10.000 steps, that is what the doctor said) without any regard if the real goal is reached. It is a rather typical effect where the System 1[6] of our brains substitutes a difficult question with a simpler, similar sounding version.

There may also be an adverse effect of bonuses at play, because many people promise themselves some kind motivating incentive ("If I go 10.000 steps today, I can eat a bag of potato chips in front of the telly tonight"). By that, the positive effect can be ruined by the unintended side effects of the measure/bonus.

The thing is that these activity devices are intended as a motivational tool ("Oh, I went 9.000 steps already, and it's only 2 PM. See if I can make 16.000 today and then have a salad."), but some people use them as the end goal ("Oh, I went 9.000 steps already, and it's only 2 PM. I can soon relax and have that well-deserved beer.").

Of course, this is no exclusive thing for weight watchers. In fact, many KPIs have exactly this effect. Numerical goals tend to become an end in themselves, which leads to unwanted effects, like when responsible managers manage quantity, not quality.

When something becomes a numerical target, the target is easily separated from what it intends to achieve[7]. Set a number of near miss reports and incentivise reporting: you can be rather sure that you get the desired number of reports, not necessarily the quality of reporting or wanted improvement. Hopkins and Maslen say in their book *Risky Rewards*[8] that this is not necessarily dishonest; it is merely the most practical way for busy people to ensure that they meet their targets. But dishonest or not, it undermines the value of the activity entirely.

So, you can manage what you measure, but very often it does not help you one tiny bit when you forget the real objectives that are behind that number and if you do not pay attention to unintended side effects from your metrics and bonuses[9].

Keep in mind Goodhart's Law, which has been phrased by Marilyn Strathem as,

"When a measure becomes a target, it ceases to be a good measure"[10].

[1] Based on a blog from October 2016, written right after returning from our annual holiday!

[2] https://www.bright.nl/nieuws/onderzoekers-afvallen-gaat-beter-zonder-activity-tracker (checked 21 July 2019)

[3] Jakicic, J.M., Davis, K.K., Rogers, R.J. et al. (2016) Effect of Wearable Technology Combined With a Lifestyle Intervention on Long-term Weight Loss: The IDEA Randomized Clinical Trial. *JAMA*, 316 (11): 1161-1171. doi:10.1001/jama.2016.12858.

[4] Stiggelbout, M., Jongert, M.W.A., Ooijendijk, W.T.M. & de Vries, S.I. (2005) *Bewegingsstimulering met Behulp van Stappentellers; Een Literatuurstudie*. TNO-rapport [KvL/IPB 2005.0781]. Retrieved 21 July 2019 from https://www.10000stappen.nl/uploaded/tno_rapport_bewegingsstimulering-geel.pdf

[5] http://www.nu.nl/gezondheid/3496628/stappenteller-helpt-daadwerkelijk-meer-bewegen.html (checked 21 July 2019)

[6] This is of course a reference to:

Kahneman, D. (2011) *Thinking Fast and Slow*. New York: Farrar, Straus and Giroux.

[7] Steven Shorrock and Tony Licu wrote a great article about the subject for Eurocontrol's *Hindsight* magazine, a few years ago. By the way, *Hindsight* is freely downloadable and contains many great articles by practitioners and safety scholars. Recommended, also for those outside of aviation!

Shorrock, S. & Licu, T. (2013) Target Culture: Lessons in Unintended Consequences. *Hindsight*, 17: 10-16. Retrieved 17 October 2019 from https://www.skybrary.aero/bookshelf/books/2336.pdf

[8] Hopkins, A. & Maslen, S. (2015) *Risky Rewards: How Company Bonuses Affect Safety*. Farnham: Ashgate.

[9] Do check the chapters discussing bonuses, incentives and the side effects of SMART.

[10] Goodhart originally phrased it as "Any observed statistical regularity will tend to collapse once pressure is placed upon it for control purposes." However, I think the later form is more telling. Sources:

Goodhart, C. (1981) Problems of Monetary Management: The U.K. Experience. In Courakis, Anthony S. (ed.). *Inflation, Depression, and Economic Policy in the West*: 111–146.

Strathern, M. (1997) Improving Ratings: Audit in the British University System. *European Review*, 5 (3): 305-321.

Green Reports, Red Talks[1]

A while ago, I talked to someone about a major reorganisation that was going on in his company. He was highly concerned about many of his colleagues who were working overtime a lot, sending e-mails in the middle of the night or during their days off and being much busier than was healthy for any of them. Another colleague agreed, mentioned that he had not seen his direct supervisor in many weeks because she was caught up in endless project meetings and they communicated exclusively through text messages and e-mail - often sent on moments way outside ordinary working hours. He agreed that some of these people at some point are going to hit the wall at full speed and suffer a serious burn out.

Both acknowledged the positive drivers in these people. These people display a large sense of ownership. They want to deliver a good job. They often go a long way to save the organisation's ass, so to speak. Even though the organisation may very well be the reason for creating their workload with unrealistic expectations, too few resources and deadlines that are too tight. Even though the organisation often does not recognise or acknowledge, let alone show appreciation for the effort these people make to deliver expected results and meet deadlines in addition to the daily work that has to go on, no matter what.

These people do not call in sick, even though they are dead tired and worn out. They are loyal to their organisation and they do not want to put additional pressure on their colleagues who would have to step in if they were to go on sick leave.

But indeed there are major dangers and risks lurking, including but not restricted to:

- loss of job satisfaction,
- a more grim atmosphere,

- cutting corners (which often may get results in the short run, but also eventually can lead to eroding of margins and lead to drift into failure),
- lower resistance (both with regard to individual health as organisational resilience),
- increased sick leave,
- burn out, and
- turnover (people starting to look for another job).

When I asked if project management and top management were aware of these things, the one who brought up the subject had a superb way of describing the disconnect between the blunt end and the sharp end of the organisation. He said:

"They report 'green', but talk about 'red'".

What he meant by this, was that all status reports 'up' in the system and to external parties appeared very positive. Production looked as usual, deadlines were met and deliverables delivered. However, outside of official meetings, in coffee breaks, and after work, people suddenly started sharing their concerns and complaints in rather clear doomsday language. As a consequence, information about looming disaster was shared informally, but never reached the official reports. At least not through the - in theory perfect - communication and reporting system established to monitor the reorganisation.

Risk matrices on the monitoring dashboards looked 'green', but this kind of 'green' is called *watermelon green*[2]. The metaphor should be clear: on the outside things look 'green' and all good to go. However, underneath that extremely thin surface, there is an enormous amount of 'red' (information about problems and looming disaster) all the way down to the core. And yet, it is the 'green' that gets reported.

Reasons for not reporting problems higher up in the system included among others:

- Things seemed to work, and this would surely be only a temporary thing, so do not act like a sissy. Just work a little harder and it will be back to normal soon.
- No one had called in sick yet, so all one could report were 'feelings' and 'hunches' and no hard numbers to build on.
- Managers do not want to be perceived as the people who do not get the stuff done - especially when this can cost them a position in the future organisation.

Earlier on in this book there was a chapter was about the perception that everything should be done to avoid 'red' indicators, or correct them as soon as possible. Without going into a deep analysis of the case above (which we cannot do anyway because we just lack tons of information), I think we can point out at least one flaw in the formal reporting system of that organisation.

It is something that applies, I think, to the reporting systems of most organisations on this globe. Most reporting systems are rather passive and absorb what they get. Only few take a truly active and critical stance. Therefore it is good advice to be suspicious of whether the 'green' is really as good as it looks. When presented with a report that has only positive information, make sure to ask: "Where is the bad news"? The watermelon metaphor even suggests that it should not be difficult to discover that critical information - you do not need to dig very deep...

Adopting this may cause more work and slower progress on the short term, but just save you so much trouble and fragility in the long run. Hidden risks may feel comfortable for a while, but not so much when they explode in your face.

###

---

[1] Based on a blog from January 2017. Many thanks to Rune Overaae for the original inspiration!

[2] Thanks to my study mate and friend Gabriel Bris for introducing me to this term!

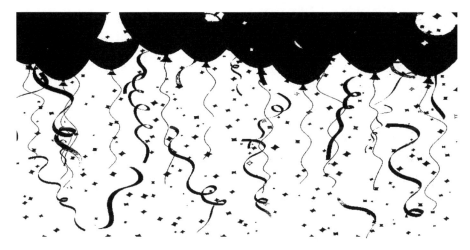

The Relevance of Outcomes[1]

-KPI- -Outcome- -Relevance-

The other day I got yet another Hallelujah message in my newsfeed. One of Norway's major construction contractors celebrated that it was a year ago that they had their last lost time injury incident and that their LTIF[2] now was at zero.

All I could do was to let out a slightly exasperated and frustrated sigh.

Shortly before, I had read James Reason's[3] latest book, *Organisational Accidents Revisited* where I noticed the quote: "The road to Hell is paved with falling LTI frequency rates". As demonstrated in major cases like Deep Water Horizon and Texas City.

For the record, let me say that it is obviously a good thing when no one has been injured as a consequence of their work. At the same time, however, it once more turned my attention to something that has keeping me busy for many years now: why are people so focused on outcomes, when they actually mean so little in terms of improvement, especially in safety.

Obsessed about Outcomes

When an incident or accident happens, in general, the consequences attract the most attention. As a rule, media (and other) reports will always tell you about the number of fatalities and injuries. From a humanitarian and empathic perspective this is only natural. It is a tragedy for the people involved to be confronted with pain, loss and sometimes life-altering experiences. When there have been severe outcomes, often regulators and enforcers get involved. Sometimes, even criminal investigators show interest to find out whether laws were broken and someone has to answer to the justice system, and maybe be punished.

There are, of course, those who show interest in pictures of damage and destruction and the dramatic stories of victims, survivors, eyewitnesses and relatives. The media are first in line. They sell these stories to the general public that loves to hear them, either shocked ("how could this happen") or with relief ("glad it was not me"). Politicians are also drawn to outcomes like flies to honey, trying to use them for their own goals (often in the media) - or trying to limit the potential damage to their position.

Last, but definitely not least, many Safety Professionals pay a lot of attention to outcomes because that is how we traditionally measure safety - or at least that is what we think we do. We register fatalities and injuries in varying degrees of seriousness. Even when organisations register information about other safety-relevant events, like material damage, near misses and observations (or more pro-active things), the information about outcomes is regarded as the most reliable or complete, very much because regulations often require that we register and report them, or because this is necessary for compensation and insurance claims.

But why?

There are many reasons why people pay much attention to outcomes. However, there are some serious professional arguments why this is not the best way to view safety.

I do not want to spend many words on this very fundamental point. First of all, we must keep in mind that absence of accidents or absence of injuries not necessarily means that things are safe. The numbers might just as well be looking good because the organisation has had an enormous amount of luck, or because incidents are not registered or reported, for whatever reason. This means that looking at outcomes, at best, is a very incomplete notion of safety (or rather the absence of safety).

Then there is the effect of randomness. Say that all accidents are reported and registered. We may believe that their importance is determined by the severity of the outcomes, but it should not be so. Just some examples:

For many years I have worked in railways. Level crossings are among the places with the highest risk on the network and regularly accidents do happen on these places. When a car is hit by a train on a level crossing, chances are that the consequences are very bad for the people in the car. The number of fatalities is usually not related to the causes for the accident, but depends on random factors like what position the car had on the level crossing at the moment of impact (is it hit full in the side, most likely killing passengers on impact, or does the train just hit the tail end, spinning the car around but not injuring people in a major way) and very much the number of people in the car (was it just one guy driving to work, a mother with children in a minivan, or a school bus).

These days, I am working with police officers. While firearm incidents are pleasantly rare in Norway, when they happen, the consequences can be very bad. Many precautions will be taken to prevent harm in these situations, but still, if someone fires a gun at one of my colleagues, a combination of many factors will make it rather random if there are no consequences (a complete miss), minor bruises (when protective gear stops the bullet) or if there is a serious, maybe even fatal injury (when the bullet somehow manages to hit a vulnerable spot).

The events (incidents, accidents) are the basically the same in these two scenarios, but the outcomes are wildly different, due to some minor factors, often sheer random ones.

So we can safely conclude that from a prevention, learning and improvement point of view, the consequences are definitely the least interesting part. As David Woods[4] and his co-authors say in their book *Behind Human Error*, outcomes are only loosely connected to processes. It is therefore better to focus on process and events than on outcomes.

Still, even though there is hardly any information for prevention in the outcomes, they are not entirely meaningless. At least outcomes do provide a sense of urgency. Alas, we must acknowledge that it is easier to prioritize and allocate resources when something really bad has happened…

A little journey through time

Are these new insights? By all means, no way!

We can start with a flashback to the 1930s. That most criticised of all safety authors, Herbert W. Heinrich[5] himself, pointed out many, many decades ago that it is the potential that lies in an event that is important. By reacting on the accident, regardless the actual outcome, one could create improvement. Besides, usually there are more accidents than outcomes, so there are more opportunities to learn and improve.

Attack the accidents, he said, and the consequences will take care of themselves. Heinrich made a clear difference between events and their consequences. Think of his work what you will, his ideas around the subject were ground breaking at the time and stand until today. Oddly, these particular thoughts of his find only little reflection in most safety metrics, even nine decades later.

Fast forward to the 1970s. Barry Turner[6] looks in his classic book *Man Made Disasters* at earlier disaster research and concludes that it is of little use in a way of preventing future disasters. Among other things, because there has been much focus on outcome. The number of fatalities of disasters, however, is very much a function of population density, not as much of what caused the disaster.

Of course, it may be very much worthwhile to use this factor in the light of exposure and fragility. Living on a volcano may give certain benefits, but when it erupts… Well, we all know how that worked for Pompeii.

This knowledge (other examples can be found for sure) has been around for decades in safety. Somehow, it appears to be little understood. As said in the introduction, people still focus mostly on outcomes.

A distorted view

Outcomes also have another negative effect because they affect how we look at a case. This is called outcome bias.

Above I mentioned the book *Behind Human Error*. It is not always an easy read, but do check out chapter 13. This entire chapter is devoted to hindsight and outcome bias. As the authors say:

> "Knowledge of outcome biases people's judgement about the processes that led up to that outcome. We react, after the fact, as if knowledge of outcome was available to operators. This oversimplifies or trivializes the situation

confronting the practitioners, and masks the processes affecting practitioner behaviour before the fact. Hindsight bias blocks our ability to see the deeper story of systematic factors which predictably shape human performance."[7]

And, of course, when outcomes are really bad, causes must have been really bad too. Intentional maybe, or reckless. But, the people in the case do not intend to produce a bad outcome. If they, like the people looking back on the event, had knowledge that their process would lead to a certain outcome, they would use this information to modify how they handled the problem.

Woods and his co-writers mention a couple of strategies of dealing with being biased by outcome. It is important to realise that information about the outcome is irrelevant to the judgement of the quality of the process that led to that outcome. Good decisions can lead to bad outcomes and good outcomes may still occur despite poor decisions.

Trying to ignore knowledge of the outcome, or alerting people about the biases are not very successful strategies to neutralise hindsight and outcome bias, however. More successful ways include having people consider alternatives to the actual outcome, or to ask people to list reasons both for and against each of the possible outcomes, comparable to a Devil's Advocate approach.

And so…

Many reasons to move away from a focus on outcomes, some of which I discussed above. That does not mean that we should not react on accidents. Of course, we have to learn from them, but we do not have to wait for someone to get hurt. To use one of the examples mentioned before, when a car swerves around the level crossing barriers to make it over before the train comes, is it really the impatient idiot driver (as some may claim), or are there things in the design that should be improved? We can very well use a near miss event to learn and do not have to wait until that next fatality.

More fundamentally, we should stop seeing safety as an outcome (i.e. a number of fatalities or injuries). Instead, we should try to adopt more fruitful ways of looking at safety.

###

[1] This was originally published on the Intelex blog in March 2017 as a preparation of a discussion of SIF phenomenon (Serious Injuries & Fatalities) which you can read in the next chapter. Find the original at:

https://blog.intelex.com/2017/03/09/measuring-safety-part-1-the-relevance-of-outcomes/

[2] LTI = Lost Time Injury, and LTIF = Lost Time Injury Frequency.

[3] Reason, J. (2016) *Organisational Accidents Revisited*. Farnham: Ashgate.

[4] Woods, D.D., Dekker, S.W.A., Cook, R., Johannesen, L., & Sarter, N. (2010) *Behind Human Error (second edition)*. Farnham: Ashgate.

[5] Heinrich, H.W. (1931) *Industrial Accident Prevention - A Scientific Approach*. New York: McGraw-Hill.

[6] Turner, B.A. (1978) *Man Made Disaster*. London: Wykeham Publications.

or

Turner, B.A. & Pidgeon, N.F. (1997) *Man Made Disaster (second edition)*. Oxford: Butterworth Heinemann.

Both are super-hard to find. Be prepared to cash out a substantial amount of money too.

[7] The quote is from the book's introduction, page 15.

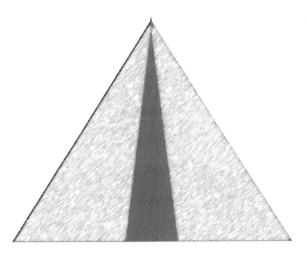

Sifting through SIF[1]

-SIF- -Constructs- -Indicators-

One specific form of 'measuring' safety is through something labelled SIF. I was blissfully unaware of the SIF-phenomenon when Todd Conklin asked me about it during our podcast[2]. Or, to be more correct, I had seen the abbreviation online, but never checked what it actually meant. Of course, I had to correct that and a quick Google search revealed among the first hits a couple of articles[3], a white paper[4] and a YouTube[5] video. Also, I found two papers by Fred Manuele from 2008 and 2013, related to the subject[6]. This is by no means a complete study (neither is 'googling' the best way to do research), but if you suffer from an information gap like I did, and you want to close it fast, it should suffice. Also, it is probably enough background for a couple of critical comments and questions that I would like to bring up.

If you are unfamiliar with SIF, you might want to get an easy introduction through that Dekra video on YouTube. But be warned, about two minutes in and I felt a little sick. Is this where we are after almost a century of safety 'science'? I wondered if SIF stands for Sad Ignorant and Frustrating, but apparently it is Serious Injuries and Fatalities. The video has its mouth full of a "New Paradigm" and acts like SIF is the best thing since sliced bread. Alas, I have a slightly more nuanced opinion. Then again, come to Norway and you may be surprised about the fact that we do very little sliced bread here, so there may be a reason why I am utterly unimpressed.

S.I.F.

In short, SIF came about when some people 'discovered' that over the past decade, incidents leading to minor injuries had shown serious improvements, while accidents leading to serious injuries and fatalities had shown much less improvement, or had even been plateauing. That was odd, they thought, because Heinrich's ratio[7] dictated (or so they thought) that attacking minor accidents would also reduce major accidents. Apparently, it did not, or at least not the way they thought it would.

The interesting thing, of course, is that this insight comes from people who had been promoting and selling a particular form of Heinrich's triangle along with behavioural programs for years. How odd that preventing slip, trips and falls did not prevent well blow outs... Research was needed!

So they studied. The Dekra White Paper documents one of these studies. For this, seven multinationals contributed a whopping average of 73 cases per company per year as basis. The conclusion: we have to change our ways. And, by the way, here is a new program to implement that will fix the problem.

In case you wondered, the program contains these actions:

1) Educate 'new model'
2) Measure SIF as one category
3) Develop processes to identify and mitigate precursors, and
4) Integrate with existing safety systems.

Is it fixed then?

The question remains, of course, if all this 'new' insight and study really was necessary.

First of all, there are several possible ways to explain or at least to wonder about the observed 'trends' (find the figures in the Dekra white paper). Just from the top of my head:

- how reliable are the numbers really (one would expect fatality-numbers to be more reliable than 'less serious' accidents),
- how does the 'trend' look in a larger historical perspective (pre-1993),
- what about changes in the larger context, like technological developments, the fall of the Iron Curtain and moving production and industrial work to low-labour-cost countries,
- the problem that it becomes harder to improve something the better it is (check the levelling of the fatality rate in Manuele's 2013 paper[8]). It will probably be easier to move from 10 to 8, than from 5 to 3.

But okay, let us assume that the trends are real. That brings us to the second point: is this really new?

For starters, they could have gone back to Heinrich's texts and studied them a bit more carefully; thinking critically about the implementation. This might have revealed something about the application of the triangle. But, given how it has become sort of mainstream safety and tradition, it may have been hard to drop that traditional view on the triangle all on their own.

There have been significant voices showing the way. Andrew Hale[9] did a great paper on the subject in the early 2000s where he offers a nuanced discussion of the subject. His conclusion says:

> "We should not think in terms of comparing major and minor injuries, but of understanding accident scenarios. We should compare completed and uncompleted accident sequences."

In other terms: stop comparing 125 strained ankles to 11 fatalities. Look at the scenarios. After that, you might use observations of slippery surfaces and uneven stairs to prevent the former and irregularities in your drilling process to prevent the latter.

Only a few years after, Erik Hollnagel told us in his book *Barriers And Accident Prevention*[10] a correct interpretation of the triangle. Instead of waiting for a 'real' accident, you can have more frequent opportunities to learn. These opportunities are also less costly because the experience is direct and the consequences smaller. There is one important condition, however:

> "In order for this approach to be effective it is, necessary that the study is confined to the minor incidents and near misses that are *directly related* to accidents at the top of the pyramid".

SIF seems to fix some of the problems of reporting outcomes and the traditional (wrong) interpretation/application of Heinrich's (in)famous iceberg. In very simple terms: applying the SIF thinking you do a variation of the triangle (often pictured in figures resembling the one above this chapter) by looking at the things that did have serious outcomes AND those incidents (with or without outcomes) that had the potential to lead to a SIF.

This is a clear improvement of the traditional collecting of all incidents and sorting them by severity of outcomes. Still, they do not go far enough in terms of scenarios. They sorted out cabbage, onions and potatoes, but due to step 2 of the "program" they still heap together apples, pears and oranges in one basket. And sorry for the lack of enthusiasm, but measures against oranges do not affect apples or pears.

S for Subjective?

Building the SIF triangle is not without other problems, however. Among these: who is to decide upon potential, and how. Let us start with the latter.

It seems to be relatively easy to define some categories to separate SIF and non-SIF. Dominic Cooper's article[11] describes one way to classify the consequences, the Dekra study[12] an alternative, and there are surely several other methods, like using risk matrices. This creates a potential problem if you want to compare SIFs across organisations, but since benchmarking is often a useless exercise anyway[13], I am not complaining too much about that and instead suggest to stop benchmarking.

The major question is, however, how to assess potential. Is this not rather arbitrary? It is not only about possible consequences, after all, you also have to think about probability or likelihood. I can think up a fatal accident for almost any event, but how realistic are those scenarios?, And where does one draw the line then? We need some assessment probability for this, but I cannot see any guidance on that. Even if there were, it is going to be pretty tricky and subjective[14]. Let us look at some examples.

The YouTube video that I watched as part of my basic research, mentions a case of slipping and falling. When this happens on a rail wagon, it is considered a SIF (makes sense, given present hazards), while slipping and falling in the parking lot is rated as low and non-SIF. But wait, slipping and falling in the parking lot can possibly be fatal if you hit your head really bad! I am not even making this up. I have a 50 year old scar on my head that can testify about a less serious outcome, but even so, there was a lot of blood and some stitches. And many years ago, a colleague of mine slipped on an ice-covered walkway in the workshop. He fell, landed on his arm and initially he shook it off, like every one of us probably would have done. In the end, however, this turned out to have been the most serious accident that year. My colleague suffered pains for a long period, had to be operated upon, had to register sick leave and had reduced use of his arm many years after. If that does not qualify as a serious injury, I wonder what.

Sticking to slips and falls, in my time at the Norwegian railroad administration, I saw dozens of incident reports where passengers slipped on icy platforms. A few led to minor injuries; most were mostly a nuisance to the 'victims'. None of them would probably have made it into a SIF category, although this is rather short-sighted, because an elderly person might have broken a hip. I know even of an accident where a 16 year old girl slipped (most likely due to ice on the platform), fell onto the subway tracks and tragically died[15].

This leads to yet another question: would a sudden realisation that a certain event should be categorized as a SIF (like the slips and falls above) lead to a re-categorization? Or does one just continue with the historic numbers? That would mean measuring with a moving target either way.

Counterfactual Reporting

That is the 'how'-problem, which deals with an issue that is encountered in most (or even all) situations where one tries to count a construct (which is what SIF is). In direct connection, we also have a 'who'-problem. This one always follows the practice of counting constructs. Different people will most likely judge cases differently. As illustrated above, knowledge of real-world cases may lead to another category, making things even more subjective. The great interrater reliability mentioned in the Dekra study only applies to that study and says little or nothing about the real world when managers, front-liners and safety people start categorizing cases on their potential.

Which, by the way, reminds me of a research project that one of my friends did in the multi-national company where she worked. Managers had to assess all incidents that had happened according to a corporate risk matrix. It turned out that people had wildly different understanding of the various categories, so 'red' for one manager or safety advisor was not 'red' for another. Additionally, there was a very strong incentive for managers to NOT score 'red' at all (and rather go for the less severe 'amber' category) because then they did not have to report to corporate… I can imagine that goals and incentives may affect SIF categorization in many organisations!

There is another odd thing. SIF programs require you to report counterfactuals: things that did not happen, but could have happened. Is that a bad thing? Not entirely, because thinking about the potential outcomes can help you to be aware of the risks you are running and how vulnerable you may be. Reporting something that did not happen is a bit silly, however, and as argued above, very subjective.

Is it all useless then?

I would not say that. It may be problematic in some aspects, but I think it is possibly a useful tool for improvement. There is some good in the message around this SIF stuff. It urges to focus on precursors, not on outcomes. In general, precursors represent unmitigated (high) risk that will eventually result in SIFs. Focus on outcomes only and you will have a blind spot. That is a wise approach, even though Heinrich said as much many decades ago and can it hardly be seen as a major new insight or paradigm shift. Well, some things just need time and a lot of repetition to sink in.

That was the good news. On the downside, it can be quite misleading as a tool for measurement. Some organisations use SIF as a metric (check for example Statoil's sustainability reports[16], they remodel it to Serious Incident Frequency). I think that is an unwise move, which may very well lead to just another form of what Fred Manuele[17] calls a "delusion". A positive SIF trend may after all give the impression of good safety, even though it really could mean that some people try to avoid 'reds' in their reports. And, with regard to subjective reporting - you can say many bad things about outcome-metrics: at least these are relatively objective…

In most cases, I am afraid that SIF programs are only a slightly improved, rebranded and polished way to sell (rather traditional) safety programs, consultancy and BBS systems.

Therefore, SIF: old wine, new bottles. Nice try, no cigar.

[1] This was published in a slightly different form for the Intelex blog. Find them via: http://mindtherisk.com/blog/165-measuring-safety-a-trilogy

[2] http://preaccidentpodcast.podbean.com/e/papod-108-not-compliantbut-not-not-compliant-carston-busch/

[3] Bell, K. (2016) Innovation in Serious Injury and Fatality (SIF) Prevention . Retrieved 20 July 2019 from http://www.ishn.com/blogs/16-thought-leadership/post/103991-innovation-in-serious-injury-and-fatality-sif-prevention

[4] Martin, D.K. & Black, A.A. (2015) *Preventing Serious Injuries & Fatalities: A New Study Reveals Precursors And Paradigms*. Retrieved 20 July 2019 from http://dekra-insight.com/images/white-paper-documents/wp_preventing-sif_us_A4.pdf

Check also:

Martin, D.K. & Black, A.A. (2015) Preventing Serious Injuries & Fatalities. *Professional Safety*, September 2015: 35-43.

http://seminarfest.asse.org/assets/docs/Don%20Martin_Preventing%20Serios%20Injuries%20and%20Fatalities_September%202015.pdf

[5] Dekra: New Paradigms in Serious Injuries and Fatalities https://www.youtube.com/watch?v=myNSOBv18uY (checked 14 October 2019).

[6] Manuele, F.A. (2008) Serious Injuries & Fatalities: A Call for a New Focus on Their Prevention. *Professional Safety*, December 2008: 32–39.

Manuele, F.A. (2013) Preventing Serious Injuries & Fatalities: Time for a Sociotechnical Model for an Operational Risk Management System. *Professional Safety*, May 2013: 51–59.

[7] Heinrich, H.W. (1931) *Industrial Accident Prevention - A Scientific Approach*. New York: McGraw-Hill.

[8] See the 2013 reference above.

[9] Hale, A.R. (2002) Conditions of Occurrence of Major and Minor Accidents: Urban Myths, Deviations and Accident Scenarios. *Tijdschrift voor Toegepaste Arbowetenschappen*, 15 (3): 34-41.

Find it online: http://www.arbeidshygiene.nl/-uploads/files/insite/2002-03-hale-full-paper-trf.pdf

The quote is from pages 39 and 40.

[10] Hollnagel, E. (2004) *Barriers And Accident Prevention*. Aldershot: Ashgate.

The quote is from page 23, I added the emphasis.

[11] Cooper, D. (2014) Reducing Serious Injuries & Fatalities: Link SIF Programs to your Safety Culture. Retrieved 15 July 2019 from http://www.ishn.com/articles/99436-reducing-serious-injuries-fatalities

[12] Reference above!

[13] See the final chapter of this book.

[14] Remember, there are no SIFs out there for you to find. SIFs are merely another safety construct, and thus by definition not objective. They rely entirely on our judgement...

[15] The tragic accident is described in among others these news items: https://www.nrk.no/ostlandssendingen/tenaring-omkom-etter-pakjorsel-av-t-banen-1.13357172 and https://www.nrk.no/ostlandssendingen/sporveien_---perrongen-ble-strodd-i-natt-1.13357613 (both checked 23 July 2019)

[16] I checked: https://www.statoil.com/en/how-and-why/health--safety-and-security.html and https://www.statoil.com/content/dam/statoil/documents/sustainability-reports/statoil-sustainability-report-2015.pdf (both checked 23 July 2019, but of course Statoil has changed names to Equinor in the meantime...)

[17] See the 2008 reference above.

Lies, Damn Lies, and…

-Statistics- -Metrics- -Manipulating-

When we see numbers or statistics, we tend to give them much attention and great weight. But beware, these can also be misleading - intentional or unintentional.

There are many, many ways to manipulate data, results and presentation. You can for example omit data, cheat, game the metrics in various ways that we discussed elsewhere in this book, showing just a selective part of the data in which you exclude possibly conflicting or contradicting information, or adjust the definitions of what to include in your counting. Often, this is not even done consciously.

There is for example that many of us are not doing particularly well with statistics. Do not be ashamed or shy, this applies to most humans, our intuitive thinking is just not up to this[1], we all suffer from innumeracy. Even the simplest statistical operations can cause us trouble. Take for example averages. We use them on a regular basis, but many people do not even realise that there are several forms of averages (e.g. mean, median, modus, weighted, rolling), and not all of them may provide useful information for what we want to say or find out.

In fact, there are plenty of cases where information about an average may be downright misleading. A person who is laying with his head in the stove and his feet in the fridge may have a 'healthy' average body temperature of 37° Celsius, but this person is most likely dead or doing really bad…

Also, the way you present the numbers may influence how people react to them. Take the example below. The left diagram shows the number of injuries associated with two different processes for a number of years. As one can imagine, the observed increase during the last year caused some major concern to the management involved.

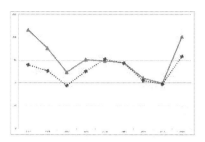
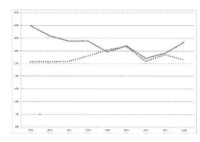

When presenting these numbers as relatives, as done in the right diagram which shows the injuries per process as a percentage of the total number of reported injuries per year, things look much less problematic. Especially the lower (dotted) line appears to be fluctuating within a certain range with a slight positive tendency in the past year. And also the upper line does not show that sharp marked increase, but also rather a movement within some natural boundaries.

Another common way to present information, which may actually be misleading, is when information is presented in a year-to-date kind of way - as in the left diagram below. This form of presentation suggests as if the subject were some kind of budget that starts on the first of January and runs until the end of December.

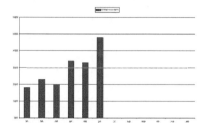
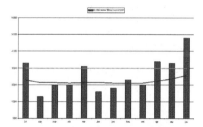

Much more useful may be to show the data in a greater context, for example by presenting the past 11, 12 or 13 months, possibly including a rolling average, as in the right diagram. While the left diagram suggests a steep and continuous increase of incidents regulated, the right diagram nuances this much more and will not give as much of an urge to have 'panic interventions' than the left - even though there is an increase.

These were only two simple ways to illustrate how the way information is presented affects how we react to it. And there are many others[2], including:

- toying with scales (different values on y-axis scales),
- cropping the graph,
- comparing huge differences,
- logarithms to make lines appear linear.

And of course, there is the widespread use of colours - we already talked about the reds and greens that are applied when something is not according to a standard/norm, or in a high/low risk area. But the suggestive colour uses can also be more subtle. Take for example the common colour schemes applied to the safety culture/maturity ladder[3].

Typically, the lower levels (pathological, reactive) are red or brown-ish, while the upper levels (proactive, generative) are green…

This chapter intends to just show a few forms of manipulation through statistics. I do not want to claim any completeness. There are some great and highly accessible books out there that discuss the 'art' of lying with statistics or misapplying them much better than I can. I suggest that you seek out some of them - your ability to review statistics and indicators more critically will benefit massively.

###

---

[1] The work of Gerd Gigerenzer is a good way to start exploring this problem, and also learning of some ways to cope with this limitation. Check for example these super readable books:

Gigerenzer, G. (2003) *Reckoning With Risk - Learning To Live With Uncertainty*. Eastbourne: Gardners Books.

Gigerenzer, G. (2014) *Risk Savvy. How to Make Good Decisions*. London: Allen Lane.

Check also the suggestions for further reading in the back of the book where you find some great, accessible and mostly entertaining titles on statistics.

[2] In addition to the books for suggested reading, as well this nice blog:

https://medium.economist.com/mistakes-weve-drawn-a-few-8cdd8a42d368 (checked 14 October 2019).

[3] Please do a quick Google search and check the pictures you find with the search phrase "safety maturity ladder".

Zero Harm: Occupational Disease[1]

-Zero- -Indicators- -Safety-

I will never forget Fred. He never knew, but he has been one of the people who helped to shape my thinking during my first years as a Safety Professional. With his lean and not even 1,70 m short frame, he did not have an impressive physical appearance, but his personality and commitment sure made up for it. He worked as a carpenter in the department that did the interior refurbishments of passenger trains at the Haarlem workshop. More importantly for me, he was a member of the emergency response and first aid team and a very active safety and health representative of his department and driving member of the Safety and Health Committee.

The Arbowet[2] points out that good safety and health management is shaped through cooperation of employer and employees. For this goal the representatives met with the workshop's management on a regular basis. Fred, however, often used to have this typical 'old fashioned' union stance that employers hardly ever had the best of intentions with the workforce. I suspect that this was one way for him to stay critical – something he did very well. In the end, however, there may have been some truth to his stance. One day he had to call in sick and after an absence of some weeks he came to my office and brought me the news he had feared all along: he had been diagnosed with mesothelioma. Within the year he passed away.

For many, many years crocidolite, the so-called 'blue asbestos', had been used to isolate coaches of passenger trains, among others, for soundproofing and shock absorbing. Long before I started as a safety advisor at the workshop, Dutch Railways had started removing this highly hazardous material from their trains, but as a carpenter, Fred had been exposed to high levels of the invisible fibres during the 1960s and 1970s when there was a serious lack of awareness, let alone adequate protection. Fred spent his last year battling the disease and responsible parties. Obviously he lost the former, worn out by chemo treatment and cancer, but he at least had the pleasure to see success in the latter helping to initiate a good compensation scheme for victims of asbestos exposure.

These days, many companies have fabulous Safety and Health Policies. Growing awareness and modern legislation have come a long way. No self-respecting business wants to do damage to man or environment and so many of them have safety goals and follow up their safety metrics. Nobody wants to have fatalities, and so the "Zero FAT" has not only become a sales slogan for healthier food, but also a safety parameter that many a company boasts with. Of course most companies do not stop at measuring FAT[3]. No, most strive for zero lost time injuries (LTI) as well. Some departments of the company I worked for previously celebrated when there had been a certain period of Zero LTIs. But how useful is this measurement, really?

Deep Water Horizon and Texas City have underlined what many of us knew before: LTIs are no parameter one should use when managing process safety. But is it not a good parameter for occupational safety then? Hardly. I will not go into any of the common and highly valid reasons (like being reactive and highly dependent on what is reported) why FAT, LTI and the like are weak safety metrics at best, and misguiding most of the time. This time, I would like to focus a bit on another drawback: there is quite a lot they do not cover!

In the first chapter of *Safety Can't Be Measured*, Andrew Townsend[4] places occupational health and safety in a larger context by looking back at human mortality since the dawn of time. One interesting observation is that only since the 1920s has life expectancy been back on the level it had been some 10.000 years earlier! More relevant here, however, is the finding that accidental death in the workplace is insignificant when compared to the total of accidental deaths: car accidents and falls at home humble even the worst work related fatality statistics. Even more interesting: deaths attributable to occupational health issues are estimated to be higher than accidental deaths in the workplace by a factor of 25! Oddly, these are not found in corporate safety statistics, targets or pithy slogans.

Also, Fred never made it into the safety statistics, except maybe in hindsight on a national level. Yet his untimely and way too early death had a clear and direct causal relation to the safety and health at the workplace since mesothelioma is very specific for exposure to crocidolite. None of the commonly used safety metrics, however, covers these cases. In my time at the workshop, I never had a FAT (yet one or two close calls), but every year we had to bury one or even several (former) colleagues who succumbed to asbestos-related diseases. Is it not ironic that if someone trips in the office, strains their ankle and has to stay at home for a day we will find them as a part of the LTI-index, but if someone dies 30 years after work exposure to asbestos there is no mention in any of the statistics?

This is only scratching the surface of what is not captured by most traditional accident/injury oriented safety metrics. There are many factors related to occupational health that may cause cancer (and eventually be fatal) like some kinds of saw dust, ceramic fibres, radiation, polycyclic aromatic hydrocarbons and other chemical substances. But there is much more that may cause permanent damage to humans without actually killing them. Take for example the number one problem for many of the slightly older colleagues in my former company: work related loss of hearing, due to exposure to noise over long periods of time. I doubt that any of them ever lost a work day because of this, but their full hearing ability will never return.

Other examples of factors that over time will lead to occupational disease may include physical strain (be it a 'mouse arm' or a worn out back), solvents (affecting the neural system) or work-related stress ('burn out' probably the fastest growing occupational disease in the Western world). There are, of course, other factors that we do not even have a full grasp of potential consequences of, like genetically modified substances and nanotechnology.

So, what would be a way forward then? First of all, we should do what has been said by several others many times before: do not stop looking back at what happened, counting injuries and incidents, but also, and especially, start looking forward. Find proactive metrics and measure most of all what your company does to create safety and health in the workplace. Use reactive data most of all as the proverbial 'litmus test' and as an opportunity for further learning and improvement.

Secondly, find metrics that cover the full spectrum of HSE(Q) and not only safety in the narrowest sense. Suggestions for widening the spectrum are mentioned above, but there are many more. Nobody knows the workplace better than your employees, so ask them. And do mind that there are factors that may escape our usual safety and health thinking, especially social issues like bullying, substance abuse, gambling or isolation at work camps or rigs.

A keyword in finding better metrics is having a focus on the hazards and the risk these hazards pose. Then we can look what to do about them and what can happen if they fulfil their potential. For starters, however, I need you to help prevent traditional safety metrics and "Zero Harm" goals becoming the Safety Professional's Number One Occupational Disease in that they blind us to some very important aspects of our job!

---

[1] This is an updated version of an article/blog that first appeared on SafetyCary in November 2013 (http://www.predictivesolutions.com/safetycary/zero-harm-is-an-occupational-disease/).

[2] The Dutch equivalent of the Safety and Health at Work Act.

[3] FAT: Fatality; LTI: Lost Time Injury

[4] Townsend, A.S. (2014) *Safety Can't Be Measured: An Evidence-based Approach to Improving Risk Reduction*. Farnham: Gower Publishing.

Only Leading Indicators Needed[1]

-Indicators- -Leading- -Lagging-

Since we concluded elsewhere in this book that accidents, injuries, LTIs and the like are a bad measure for safety, one may think that one can do away with them and instead of these lagging indicators must steer on leading indicators only.

As often in safety, there is not a binary choice of one or the other - it is very much a case of both and each in the right application and context[2]. I am definitely inclined to agree that indicators that tell you about the creation of safety are the most valuable. Indicators about work-as-done. Indicators about inputs, throughputs and outputs of your processes.

But lagging outcome indicators are necessary as the proverbial litmus test - mind you, by way of an indicator, not as a performance indicator or even KPI, although you will quite often find them as such. They can signalise that something is wrong in the system, after all something unwanted happened. Another reason for not discarding them is that you are most likely recording them already (because of regulatory or other obligations), so you might just as well use them for what they are worth (which is not that much, but still).

There is another point to make. What is leading and what is lagging? Are near misses and precursor incidents leading indicators? One can argue that they are because they enable you to take proactive steps before a 'real' accident with bad consequences happens. On the other hand one may argue that they are lagging, because you can only report them and act on them after they have happened.

Do not bother too much about putting stickers on your indicators[3]. Erik Hollnagel wrote,

> "Managing something requires being able to observe or detect it, being able to determine when it is getting out of hand, and being able effectively to introduce countermeasures or mitigating it"[4].

Whether we call them leading or lagging (or nothing at all), find good indicators that say something about what you do, and that help you to improve.

---

[1] Based on Myth 75 from *Safety Myth 101*.

[2] Like when you are driving a long distance in your car. You may want to have information how much fuel is left in your tank in addition to the information about the distance that you have travelled already, and how much further you have to go.

[3] The 'what's in a name' effect is something closely connected to all kinds of constructs; for example with regard to causes.

Andrew Hopkins considered leading and lagging "meaningless" labels, because they are used inconsistently, and mainly are used to draw attention to different things in different contexts. On page 465 of the paper mentioned below, he says, "Whether they be described a lead or lag is ultimately of little consequence."

In the same issue of *Safety Science*, John Wreathall wrote a reaction on Hopkins' paper which he titled *Leading? Lagging? Whatever!* stressing the implicit underlying models of safety and that the common leading/lagging distinction is much clearer in linear relationship

Hopkins, A. (2009) Thinking About Process Safety Indicators. *Safety Science*, 47: 460-465. doi:10.1016/j.ssci.2007.12.006.

Wreathall, J. (2009) Leading? Lagging? Whatever!. *Safety Science*, 47: 493-494. doi:10.1016/j.ssci.2008.07.031.

[4] Hollnagel, E. (2004) *Barriers and Accident Prevention*. Aldershot: Ashgate.

Safety Incentive Schemes[1]

-Incentives- -Bonus- -Side effects-

Incentive schemes[2] are often offered as a solution for a variety of issues. After all, people do things because of what happens when they do them. This is the basis for the simple behavioural ABC model of Activators, Behaviour and Consequences[3]. If the consequences are desirable for people, they are likely to do the things necessary to accomplish those consequences. To put things into the language of economists, people do things because of the incentives.

We have all heard of the stick and carrot as tools to get things done. Incentives are of course the fancy word for carrot. Positive stimulation helps to get people display wanted behaviour, so incentive schemes must be good is the thought.

In the safety world, incentive schemes are for example used to stimulate reporting of incidents, near misses and the like. There are many examples for this, like awarding reports with a cake or some kind of a gift coupon. This can be done either by randomly drawing a report in a certain period of time, or by having some criteria for awarding reports that led to the greatest improvement. The most extreme even add a safety bonus to the payment based upon a minimum number of incidents on a location within a set period. The latter means that there is a risk of awarding bonuses based on pure chance or luck, or even awarding cheating when accidents are not reported but rather brushed under the carpet to keep the bonus safe.

Incentives are pretty much the tool of choice of many traditional economists - it is what many of them look for as a main explanation for decisions and actions[4]. People like Daniel Pink argue forceful against the use of incentives. He finds it a tool that does not fit our situation in the 21st Century. Incentives work in some circumstances, but in others they do not work or they even do harm. According to Pink this is one of the biggest ignored findings of social science. And so there is a major mismatch between what science knows and what business does. Most of our Human Resource systems are built around extrinsic motivators like carrots and sticks. This was fine for many 20th Century tasks, but for 21st Century, tasks this mechanistic approach should not be the main way to go anymore.

Also psychologist Barry Schwartz[5] has a strong message with regard to incentives. In his book and his TED Talks he argues that rules and incentives may make things better in the short run, but they create a downward spiral that makes things worse in the long run. Moral skill is chipped away by an overreliance on rules while the moral will to do the right thing is undermined by incentives.

As often, it is neither black nor white as Hopkins and Maslen[6] show in their thorough discussion of bonus schemes and their effect on (process) safety. One important question to ask is how effective incentive schemes really are and what unanticipated and unwanted effects they may have.

One major problem is that incentive schemes are almost always bound to be subject to the *Law of Unintended Side Effects*, especially when meeting a certain number becomes a goal in itself[7]. When something becomes a numerical target, the target easily gets separated from what it intends to achieve. Set a number of near miss reports and incentivise reporting: you can be rather sure that you get the desired *number* of reports, not necessarily the quality of reporting or wanted improvement[8]. Hopkins and Maslen state that this is not necessarily dishonest; it is merely the most practical way for busy people to ensure that they meet their targets. But dishonest or not, it undermines the value of the activity entirely.

No incentive system is ever smart enough, every incentive system can be subverted by ill-intend. Barry Schwartz says that excessive reliance on incentives demoralises professional activity. Firstly, they demoralise the people engaged in the activity because it creates people who are 'addicted' to incentives and then people do a job only when they get paid for it. And on the other hand, people who actually want to do a good job bail out, mentally or altogether. Secondly, incentives demoralise the activity itself - they take the morality out of the practice[9].

Wrapping things up towards a solution: people do respond to incentives, understanding this is an important step in solving problems. But you also have to understand which incentives work and what works in what situation. Incentives are not only financial. Incentives can be so much more than money. Daniel Pink lists autonomy, mastery and purpose (things on a higher level in Maslov's hierarchy) as much more important. In fact often non-financial incentives are much more effective, and considerably cheaper. The best advice is to treat other people with decency. As Levitt and Dubner say: "It is most powerful when least expected, like when things have gone wrong"[10]. When it comes to reporting, the best award is the (visible or felt) improvement that comes from it, so reacting promptly works. And let it be said that even deciding to do nothing, provided one explains why, may be experienced as a reward because it acknowledges the report and reacts on it in a serious and honest way.

In order to find out, one has to get inside people's minds and find out what really matters to *them*. Once more: do safety WITH them, not TO them. Sometimes the incentives are not obvious and most of the time you will not find out by asking, because people say what they think you would like to hear and not what they really do think (the difference between declared and revealed preferences). There is often a major gap between these. Therefore, do not listen what people say, watch what they do.

When designing an incentive scheme to 'herd' people into doing the right thing (even when they do it for the wrong reasons - possibly your incentive) it is important to figure out what actually works and not only what you *believe* should work. The key is to think less about the ideal behaviour of imaginary people in the presumed situation and more about the actual behaviour of real people in their context. Real people are much more unpredictable than imaginary people. Remember also that the people whose behaviour you are trying to change[11] often do not think like you and therefore may react differently than you might expect.

A simple set of rules for a working incentive scheme (if you are convinced that you need one):

1. Figure out what people really care about, not what they say.

2. Incentivise them on the dimensions that are valuable to them, but cheap for you to provide.

3. Pay attention to how people respond. Learn from feedback and try to improve your scheme.

4. Try to create incentives that switch the frame from adversarial to cooperative.

5. Do not imagine that people will do something just because it is the 'right' thing to do.

6. Rest assured that some people will do everything to beat the system, often in ways that you have not imagined.

---

[1] Based on Myth 74 from *Safety Myth 101*.

[2] I am really only going to scratch the surface in this chapter. There is a lot of recommended stuff to read here, among others the book about bonuses and safety by Andrew Hopkins and Sarah Maslen, Barry Schwartz's *Why We Work* and also things that I have not had the chance yet to explore like Daniel Pink's *Drive*. If you can read Dutch then *Intensieve Menshouderij* is a clear must.

[3] Based on the work of B.F. Skinner, and used in most Behaviour Based Safety approaches. Skinner's insight is that behaviour is strongly influenced by the consequences and his research emphasized the importance of positive reinforcers.

Skinner, B.F. (1953) *Science and Behaviour*. New York: The Macmillan Company.

[4] If you are looking for an entertaining way to explore some of these ideas, pick just one of the *Freakonomics* books (alternatively the *Undercover Economist* series). One of the main premises is

that incentives are the cornerstones of modern life. But, mind you, Levitt and Dubner do not promote mindless incentive schemes. They have a critical eye open at the same time.

[5] His book *Why We Work* is recommended reading. You can get a good sense of his message by watching one of his TED Talks that I mentioned in the main text. There are several, but why not start with this one from 2009 titled *Our Loss Of Wisdom*:

https://www.ted.com/talks/barry_schwartz_on_our_loss_of_wisdom

[6] Hopkins, A. & Maslen, S. (2015) *Risky Rewards: How Company Bonuses Affect Safety*. Farnham: Ashgate.

[7] See for example Chapter 6 of *Think Like A Freak* (sides 130 - 135) for some examples of well-meant, but spectacularly backfiring incentive schemes. Especially the Mexico City example is both tragic and very funny and a great example that one must be clear over that people often react differently than policy makers think they do. People have their own goals and they are very creative in reaching them!

My friend Bart Vanraes pointed me to a story in *The Guardian*. Short version: Kelly, a dolphin from The Institute of Marine Mammal Studies in Mississippi learned how to retrieve trash from the water. Kelly was rewarded a fish per piece of trash. This went well until it was discovered that Kelly hid trash on the bottom of the river and delivered small pieces (each of which was rewarded with a fish) thereby optimising her reward.

https://www.theguardian.com/science/2003/jul/03/research.science (checked 25 July 2019)

Similar stories are known about rats, and then I am not even talking about the office-based kind…

[8] One funny (or sad) anecdote in that regard comes from an oil and gas contractor that worked for one of the major players in the sector. This multinational had included safety goals in the contract which not only covered the standard LTI-frequencies, but also included some more leading indicators. Specifically the Safety Bonus for the crew was connected to a minimum of 750 reported near misses or observations on the location. The reports from the location flooded in, but were usually of a level that did little to improve safety or health significantly. One typical example said "There is chewing gum stuck on the inside wall of the elevator." The real irony was that at the time that this specific 'case' was reported the multinational had discontinued the Safety Bonus two years earlier, but the site had not been informed…

[9] We assume that extrinsic motivation and intrinsic motivation are complementary, but often the extrinsic motivation replaces the intrinsic motivation.

[10] Taken from Chapter 6 of *Think Like A Freak* which was a major inspiration for these final paragraphs. Levitt and Dubner place great weight on incentives in general (they even say that incentives are the cornerstone of modern life!), but keep a critical mind to what works and what does not.

Levitt, S.D. & Dubner, S.J. (2014) *Think Like A Freak: The Authors of Freakonomics Offer to Retrain Your Brain*. New York: William Morrow.

[11] You may want to keep in mind that changing the circumstances people are in often is much more effective than trying to change their behaviour through incentives and the like.

Benchmarking Is Good for Safety[1]

-Benchmark- -Compare- -Learning-

Among managers, and probably even more among (management) consultants, it is very fashionable to compare your company (or department) to others as a way of trying to determine how well one is doing and also often to get ideas or 'best practices'[2] from others.

In principle, benchmarking sounds like a sensible thing to do. After all, it should give a possibility to learn from others. It may save you time to discover and develop certain things for yourself. It can show how you deviate from organisations that are comparable to you and thereby gives you kind of a yardstick to see if you are on the right level of safety (or if you are 'too safe' which can cause your company to lose a competitive edge). When done right, benchmarking can indeed have these advantages. When done wrongly, it may lead to other results.

There are basically two things that you can benchmark:

- Compare your results to other companies.
- Look at what others are doing to learn from their 'best practices'.

The second point is rather self-explanatory, but why would you want to compare your own results with others? To say things crudely, this is either driven by Ego (which can take the form of *"Look how great we are"* or the more modest *"We are not doing so bad compared to others"*) or Envy (*"I want what they have"*).

Then there is the question what organisation you are going to benchmark against. Two of the main directions here are:

- 'The Best'.
- An organisation (or multiple organisations) that can be roughly compared to yours.

It seems to make sense to benchmark against 'the best'. After all, that gives you something to strive for with ambitious goals and you can probably learn most from them. It raises a couple of questions, however, because often it is rather debatable how one should determine 'the best'.

Quite often, one looks at so-called 'industry leaders' which are usually those who have lowest injury or accident rates or those who proclaim themselves to be the best. Neither of these criteria should be reason enough to look at them. From the latter group, you can mainly learn a good deal about window dressing, the former will offer even less because injury rates say little.

Finding 'the best' may be rather difficult because you will often need to define specific criteria. You may end up with things that you would like to look at that are not easily available elsewhere. You may find them in organisations roughly comparable to yours, but there is still the context to consider. Something that works very well in one organisation may not work in yours[3]. There is no one-size-fits-all in safety and neither do we have any Silver Bullets. Which brings us back to the other part of benchmarking, namely *what* we benchmark.

Although it is implicit a part of many tendering processes, for example when contractors are asked to give their LTI-rates, benchmarking results against others is quite often a useless activity. One important reason for this bold statement is that the context matters. Even if you use relative numbers (e.g. a metric per working hours, or per production volume), there are many variables that affect results. Therefore, it will be hard to find an organisation that is suitable and comparable in a way that comparison of results actually makes sense. The only really sensible benchmark of these frequencies would be against yourself, like comparing to the past few years. But even there context is essential. After all, most likely the work will not have been exactly the same, there may have been changes in methods, projects, resources, and so on. Then there is the question of what results you are going to benchmark, but I am not going to discuss the uselessness of injury rates once more, just take that as a given.

One major problem is that benchmarking is usually focused on numbers that are taken out of their context. Benchmarking is often a question of looking at the grass which is greener on the other side, but rarely is it considered that your organisation may be rather into flowers or vegetables and that grass (no matter how green) is not really relevant at all...

Taking this to the realm of safety, one also has to be careful of what one benchmarks. Sectors and even companies within one sector have specific challenges and should specify indicators that say something about *their* business. Just copying and comparing indicators may give an entirely wrong picture and even lead to a false sense of security[4] - or useless actions that are ineffective at best, but are also a waste of resources and can actually make things worse.

Often benchmarks are a very reductionist exercise where one looks at just one item in isolation. That, however, is a serious mistake. As systems thinking pioneer Russell Ackoff[5] taught us many years ago, you cannot get best results by managing the parts and then believe that you are managing the whole. When you take the best parts and put them all together, you do *not* get the best whole. But we keep believing that, and that is what benchmarking is all about! The only thing that should be appropriately benchmarked is the whole - not the parts! Deming told us that copying without knowledge and understanding of principles is a problematic thing to do, and already DeBlois warned about this in 1926[6]!

Looking at what others are doing and trying to adopt some of their actions for yourself is often a smart thing to do, especially when you look at organisations that are struggling with the same challenges as yours. In those cases it is often easier to determine if their 'best practices' may work for you. But it can be useful to look also at totally different companies (regardless if they are stamped as 'the best' or not) because there surely is a lot to learn there - as long as you seriously consider whether a 'best practice' will actually work in your organisation or if you need to adapt them in some way.

Please do mind that the benchmarking errors described above are not limited to safety. They are regrettably seen repeated constantly in many areas of business. Consultants either knowingly or unknowingly use this type of benchmarking error to sell new ideas. Based on the discussion above, I would like to propose a simple benchmarking matrix which may guide further endeavours in benchmarking.

	The 'Best'	Comparable organisation
Results	Do not! Ever.	Reluctantly. Do mind the metrics and the context
'Best' practices	Only with the greatest care	Might be useful, but mind the context

---

[1] Based on Myth 78 from *Safety Myth 101*.

[2] I am using 'best practice' here because it is a rather established term, but only with the greatest of reluctance.

[3] Niels Pfläging has written a very interesting blog that highlights why benchmarking and learning from 'the best' may not work. Upon hearing how successful and innovative organisations work, many people feel inspired or motivated, but fail to implement the lessons in their own organisation. The main reason for this, according to Niels is the way we think about people and what drives them. The views of Adam Smith and Fredrick Taylor are still prevalent. As Niels says: "As long as we operate in command-and-control mode, people will usually show obedient, dependent, or even idiotic behaviour". And if we believe that this will not work at our organisation because people are not ready for this, the good example may even become a barrier for improvement! Read the full text at: http://vision.haufe.de/blog/en/why-we-cannot-learn-a-damn-thing-from-semco-or-toyota/

[4] We all know the problem with companies that used LTIs as the main metric for safety and thereby not paying any attention to process safety (points of criticism after Texas City and Deep Water Horizon). Hopkins and Maslen mention various other examples in their book, for example loss of containment which is a fine indicator for many companies in the process industry, but maybe not the best for those whose main business is transport.

Hopkins, A. & Maslen, S. (2015) *Risky Rewards: How Company Bonuses Affect Safety*. Farnham: Ashgate.

[5] Despite the bad sound quality, I warmly recommend watching the following key note by Ackoff. Make sure you watch all four parts:

https://www.youtube.com/watch?v=_pcuzRq-rDU

[6] Lewis A. DeBlois was the first Safety Director of DuPont and quite influential in the early safety movement. The quote:

> "We therefore say to the reader, if a newcomer or an early beginner, by all means realize that in the general phases of the work, especially stimulative work, there is practically nothing new and that all 'new schemes' are usually but variants of what has been tried many times before. Instead of spending time and money on them in the first flush of enthusiasm, learn first where they have been tried already and with what success; also determine whether they can be successfully transplanted. Above all, stick hard to the fundamental requirements without which no schemes or 'stunts', however captivating they appear at first, can be made effective." (p.33)

DeBlois, L.A. (1926) *Industrial Safety Organization for Executive and Engineer*. New York: McGraw-Hill.

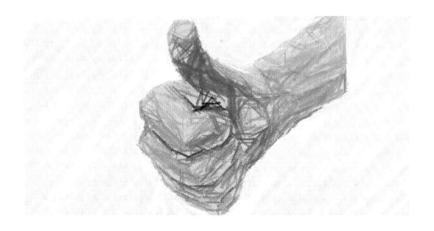

Alternatives and Suggestions

Now that you have reached the end of the book, I like to assume that you have gathered some ways to think differently about safety measuring, indicators and goals. That means that the main mission of the book is accomplished. A variety of critical ways to think and talk about measures will surely help you to find better ways. But wait, there is more, because this final chapter aims to add a few additional suggestions and alternatives to your potential future toolbox.

Try to capture the river

As we saw in the introduction, safety is a complex matter that should not be dumbed down into a simple metric, especially when that metric is one with very weak information about safety (e.g. an LTI-index). Hard as it may be, if you want to have a better feel about how you are doing at safety, you should try to capture some of that complexity and acknowledge that this will only be a glimpse of reality, but at least a glimpse that leads you to better questions.

Capturing some of the complexity can be done by embracing various views. Early on in the book we discussed a few different ways to view safety. These different views can provide a good start. Capturing some of the complexity also requires you to create a richness in reporting. One thing that helps in creating richness is to use a variety of metrics, all of which provide us a different facet of safety. In addition, it is advisable to reach beyond metrics and employ to a greater degree storytelling as a way of adding richness to your measures.

Tell stories

At one point, in an organisation I worked in, we got the opportunity to influence the safety part of the management reporting tool. Traditionally, units would report in the typical metrics, like number of personal injuries and reported incidents in a number of categories. We scrapped all that. Instead of reporting numbers (which we could pick from the databases ourselves, in case we felt like it), we required underlying units to tell us stories: What do you see? What are the trends and developments? What challenges are you dealing with? What goes well? What have you learned? How are you handling things? Are things happening you feel others should learn from?

This new way of working needed some getting used to and the first month we actually returned quite a few reports that followed the traditional approach of summing up numbers with the message "This is not what we asked for. Tell us what you see and what you learn from it". Over the period of a year, there was a really nice development and instead of 'dumb' reporting, we transited into a process of reflection and sharing.

Should we measure at all?

Trying to measure the traditional way with metrics is a suboptimal (at best) approach for complex properties or phenomena like safety or culture. A metric will provide you limited information and more often than not mislead you. A better way of 'knowing' is to aim for rich descriptions.

This gives rise to so-called "soft measures"[1], which provides us with richer information through stories and descriptions. And if you do indeed measure and use metrics, use them to initiate stories and most importantly: do not regard a metric as some kind of an answer. Rather regard them as the starting point of a discussion and a way to ask questions.

Make it dynamic

LTI scores and the like tend to be a steady item in management reports, but does it need to be that way? Indicators need not be on scorecards forever. Rather shift them out to highlight various problems and then focus on other things for a period, as required by business and other needs.

One reason for a varied approach is that these numbers get stale pretty quickly - even when they seem to present 'good news'. Changing them out from time to time (or having a rotating roster for them) keeps them fresher and more interesting. Also, varying the metric may accommodate a balance between limited space in management reports and the need for a variety to capture at least a glimpse of the complexity.

What does the metric NOT tell us?

A subject discussed earlier on in the book, is to wonder about what the numbers are NOT telling you. It is wise to try to see both sides of a story. This requires you to look actively for the bad news if it does not come to you.

A while ago, I attended a presentation of a safety representative who talked about the safety work in his unit. While he of course discussed challenges and problems, the general tone was very positive. The unit was doing a really good job. Management involved workers. Proactive measures were taken. However, this safety rep concluded, he was worried. When he looked at other comparable units, he noticed that there had been a number of cases of whistle blowing. There had been none in his unit. He wondered whether this was due to all the good work that was being done, or whether there was something underneath that prevented signals like these come to the fore. He hoped for the former, but if the latter was the case, he was really worried.

Benchmarking is so 1999

As argued in the previous chapter - be reluctant to benchmark. Hard as this is, supress the inclination to compare your performance (however you choose to define it) with others. Safety is not a competition[2].

Find your rumble strips

Good measures, whether these are metrics or stories, should provide you with early warnings. Early warnings that give you an opportunity to correct and improve when you are approaching a critical safety margin. To say it with Todd Conklin's metaphor: What are your "rumble strips"? When do you get a signal that you are still on the road, but approaching a situation where you may end up in the ditch unless you perform some adjustments?

These early warnings may be surprisingly out of the ordinary. For example, a client of mine was going through a reorganisation. They were worried about work pressure and people burning out. Their HR department thought they had control since they were monitoring sick leave and turnover metrics. These are not the "rumble strips" you should be looking for, however, since you are way too late. When asked, workers came with creative signals that work pressure was nearing critical levels: they would notice that some colleagues brought toothbrushes to the office (indicating night work and sleep overs), that they would receive text messages and mails late at night or in the weekend, and importantly the subjects that people talked about at the coffee machine.

To discover important but untypical indicators like these, involve your people. Ask workers, supervisors, managers and use their ingenuity and knowledge of the messy everyday work. Ask what they notice and what makes sense to them, rather than thinking what looks good on the quarterly report.

But what if we must?

One final problem. What then, if you have to report on certain indicators, like reporting fatalities to the regulator, or reporting LTIs to the corporate level? After all, compliance is one of the main reasons for measuring. As much as we would like to do without this kind of reporting, we often have to report these things. The recommended attitude is to make the best of it. You will be recording this kind of information anyway (at least

I expect you do), but put as little as possible effort into the metric and find something useful that you can steer on instead, or in addition.

Remember: this is not easy…

Make no mistake, all those questions that you have developed while reading this book and all the alternatives that are suggested may not be popular. These alternatives will be harder to sell to management and others than slick, numerical metrics. These alternatives do have a number of issues connected to them. Not to scare you off in the very last second, but to prepare you for the resistance there is or will be:

- You are rocking the boat and challenging the status quo. Some of these measures and tools have been used for many, many years. Everyone else is using them. Why should we change our ways then?
- Soft measures and stories lack the attraction of apparently easy to grasp metrics, colours and smileys.
- Providing nuanced and rich stories that show several sides of the story may seem 'uncertain' and difficult. Managers (and others) like simple, crisp and clear answers.
- The alternative ways of reporting and providing information cost more effort, both to produce and to process and understand them. That is probably not popular in a busy day's work.
- And do not forget that measuring does have advantages. It serves us well in many cases.

Therefore: find a balance! Combine measurements with rich sources of information, ask questions and do not try to change the world in one day. Culture is best nurtured by one little drop at a time.

<hr>

[1] A good paper on the subject, including some critical remarks about "soft measures" and how they often are used:

Martin, G.P., McKee, L. & Dixon-Woods, M. (2015) Beyond metrics? Utilizing 'Soft Intelligence' for Healthcare Quality and Safety. *Social Science & Medicine*, 142: 19-26. doi: 10.1016/j.socscimed.2015.07.027.

[2] Despite what some make of it and praise the competitive elements to create a 'drive' for safety work.

Further Reading

-Critical- -Expanding- -Mind-

Below you find a selection of books to the topics in this book that I have found to be very useful or enlightening, and sometimes also just entertaining. I recommend to find some of the titles and widen your horizon!

About statistics, both understanding them and abusing them:

Blauw, S. (2018) *Het Bestverkochte Boek Ooit (met deze Titel): Hoe Cijfers ons Leiden, Verleiden en Misleiden.* Amsterdam: De Correspondent.[1]

Huff, D. & Geis, I. (1954) *How To Lie With Statistics.* New York: Norton.

Paulos, J.A. (1989) *Innumeracy. Mathematical Illiteracy and its Consequences.* New York: Hill and Wang.

Reuben, A. (2019) *Statistical: Ten Easy Ways to Avoid Being Misled By Numbers.* London: Constable.

Smith, G. (2015) *Standard Deviations: Flawed Assumptions, Tortured Data, and Other Ways to Lie with Statistics.* New York: Harry N. Abrams.

---

[1] An English version is in the works!

About understanding science (and statistics) and applying them in risky and everyday situations:

Bauer, T., Gigerenzer, G. & Krämer, W.[2] (2014) *Warum Dick Nicht Doof Macht Und Genmais Nicht Tötet - Über Risiken Und Nebenwirkungen Der Unstatistik*. Frankfurt: Campus.

Gigerenzer, G. (2014) *Risk Savvy. How to Make Good Decisions*. London: Allen Lane.

Goldacre, B. (2009) *Bad Science (enhanced edition)*. London: Fourth Estate[3].

Goldacre, B. (2014) *I Think You'll Find It's A Bit More Complicated Than That*. London: Fourth Estate.

About bureaucracy and traditional management, its side effects and metrics for the sake of metrics.

Alvesson, M. & Spicer, A. (2016) *The Stupidity Paradox: The Power and Pitfalls of Functional Stupidity at Work*. London: Profile Books.

Dekker, S.W.A. (2018) *The Safety Anarchist. Relying on Human Expertise and Innovation, Reducing Bureaucracy and Compliance*. Milton Park: Routledge.

Graeber, D. (2015) *The Utopia of Rules. On Technology, Stupidity, and the Secret Joys of Bureaucracy*. Brooklyn/London: Melville House.

Muller, J.Z. (2018) *The Tyranny of Metrics*. Princeton: Princeton University Press.

Rose, T. (2016) *The End of Average: How We Succeed in a World That Values Sameness*. New York: Harper Collins.

Peters, J. & Pauw, J. (2004) *Intensieve Menshouderij - Hoe Kwaliteit Oplost In Rationaliteit*. Schiedam: Scriptum.

About incentives and how they work for us, or against our goals:

Hopkins, A. & Maslen, S. (2015) *Risky Rewards: How Company Bonuses Affect Safety*. Farnham: Ashgate.

Levitt, S.D. & Dubner, S.J.[4] (2014) *Think Like A Freak: The Authors of Freakonomics Offer to Retrain Your Brain*. New York: William Morrow.

Schwartz, B. (2015) *Why We Work*. London: TED Books/Simon & Schuster.

---

[2] Check the website this book is based on: www.unstatistik.de

[3] A short overview of the book can be found on its Wikipedia page. A HUGE collection of bad science can be found on Goldacre's website: http://www.badscience.net/

[4] Check also their website: www.freakonomics.com

The Author

Carsten has studied Mechanical Engineering, Safety and Human Factors. He also spent some time at Law School, but prioritised moving to Norway above graduating. He has over a quarter of a century of experience in HSEQ Management at various levels in organisations from various railway and oil & gas related companies in The Netherlands, United Kingdom and Norway. Currently he works as Senior Advisor Occupational Safety at Politidirektoratet. Specialties include incident investigation, risk assessment, management systems, HSEQ steering, organisational change as well as training and coaching of professionals and managers. He speaks regularly on seminars and conferences about a variety of topics. He is involved in the Lund University Human Factors and System Safety program as a tutor. His main research interests include the history of knowledge development and discourse in safety.

Carsten started his own website/firm *Mind The Risk* as a platform for professional knowledge sharing (and possibly future service provider for clients). He was part of the organising team for the 2014 EHSQ Elite symposium and he has been an active member of the Dutch Society for Safety Science (NVVK) for quite a while. He became a regular contributor to their quarterly magazine doing among other things reviews of professional literature, and entered the board of editors for their magazine from late 2015 on. He regularly provides articles or blogs and is active on various professional forums. Previous books include the well-received *Safety Myth 101* and *Veiligheidsfabels 1-2-3*. Future ambitions include becoming a lecturer on Safety Mythology. Meanwhile he works on a book about the life and work of safety pioneer H.W. Heinrich.

Other fields of expertise include progressive rock (you can find some writings on the subject online), single malt whisky and fantasy literature. Having bought an old large house, he is still learning more about do-it-yourself than he ever wanted.

October 2019

Acknowledgements

While I wrote this little book, I have to acknowledge the many persons who contributed to its evolution and contents - knowingly or not. It is good practice to state that all the mistakes are mine, and they are. Tell me if you find them. I would like to thank the following, in no particular order and with a high likelihood of forgetting someone (sorry!): Martijn Flinterman, Beate Karlsen, Irene Thaule, Alan Quilley, Cary Usrey, Todd Conklin, David van Valkenburg, Bart Vanraes, Jean-Christophe Le Coze, my HFSS-group, in particular Fabian Landherr, the HEACH-crew, the participants of the Masterclass at Nyenrode in May 2019 who provided inspiration to do this, and obviously my wonderful wife, Annemarije, and my family. Special thanks to Tristan for doing an awesome job on the proof reading!

Manufactured by Amazon.ca
Bolton, ON

11125261R00066